MAYHEM, MURDER AND MEDICINE

PRISON NURSE

ELLEN KANE

For information contact:
Ellen Kane
2711 N Sepulveda Ave
Box #613
Manhattan Beach, CA 90266

Paperback ISBN 978-1-54398-604-4
eBook ISBN 978-1-54398-605-1

Cover and sketches designed by Daniel Pagan
Danpagandraws.com

Copyediting by Flo Selfman
www.WordsalaMode.com

Contents

Dedication:

I dedicate this book to my three sons:
Brendan, Seamus and Miles, and our dog Coach.

Introduction

The Big House, aka Stillwater State Prison, was kind of in my neighborhood. Less than a mile away, it was high up on a hill overlooking the St. Croix River in Bayport, about 30 miles northeast of Minneapolis. The hundred-year-old building held a magnificent view for the 1400 inmates doing time inside. That was part of my reasoning for deciding to work there—the history, the close proximity and the simple fact that I needed to eat.

Recently divorced, with three little kids and a nursing degree, I needed a job, a "good State job" as my father would say. I figured that in any institution where the residents were not allowed to go home, there had to be some type of nursing positions.

I decided to call and "No," there weren't any openings for an RN because the nurses never left, but "Yes," they would interview me because the supervisor could see a maternity leave on the horizon.

I walked to the conveniently located prison compound and was met by the head nurse. She immediately ushered me through two sets of gates that were controlled by guards. One was automatic and was operated by a guard in a glass booth. A second guard opened the other gate with a large brass key. Later I found out that I had been escorted through the "turnkey."

The head nurse walked me down a long flagstone hallway where I passed four very large cell halls. I could see four levels of cells called "tiers" floor to ceiling but we didn't go inside the halls. My tour ended in the Health Services building, outside the main prison building but still inside the prison compound.

At the end of my interview I was hired by the head nurse to replace the part-time night nurse during her pregnancy. It was a six-month temporary position, but I didn't care. I knew that if I got in, some other work would come along. My six-month hire turned into ten years of State service.

My life was pretty chaotic around the time I went to work in the prison. Little did I know that a maximum-security prison would provide a certain sense of calm while I struggled with the challenges in my personal life. My marriage was breaking up. I had three little boys at home, two still in diapers, and my future, including financial, was uncertain.

When I entered the prison, the contrast was immediate. Within those walls, everything was structured and controlled, marked by the chiming of bells and the sound of buzzers. While I was inside, unlike most of the inmates, I felt relief. I had a job to do, I could feed my family and, it gave me a measure of control that I wasn't experiencing in my daily life.

My mother opposed the idea from day one but my brother Dennis said, "You'll love it, it's like working in a bar." He was a probation officer and enjoyed working with the challenging teens. He taught them basketball and I became acquainted with his kids later as adults and still in the revolving door of the correction system. Sadly, his kids' tickets were written at birth.

Inmates are real people, and the majority of them were good people who did bad things. Most did their time and went home, while others are still doing their time and will never go home.

I knew it was time to leave correctional nursing when I could see myself losing my sense of humor. I knew it was time to leave the prison system when my patience with both inmates and staff had grown thin. For the next twenty years I practiced as a research nurse in areas of AIDS/HIV and inflammatory bowel diseases specifically Crohn's and ulcerative colitis.

Still living in Minnesota and running clinical trials out of two county hospitals, I would encounter many familiar faces from my prison days, ex-inmates who remembered me and were happy to reminisce on our lives behind bars. But there were many who didn't recognize me though I knew them. Maybe I was out of context to them or maybe they were high or maybe they were trying to forget their past and I was in their past.

For years it wasn't polite to bring up my prison stories at family functions, or so my mother thought, but my good friend Bev would listen and was very sad when I left corrections; she was my captive audience while we walked daily after work. My oldest son Brendan and all his friends were also disappointed. He was waiting for the day he could have a tour but he had to be eighteen years old and he was only twelve when I resigned.

During those years my brother Kevin, a published poet, would encourage me to write my prison stories down. He would say, "You're going to forget." Kevin was disciplined in his writing as well as in his life; he continuously edited and published a literary magazine for fifteen years and had three books of poems published as well. He's retired now and still writes daily. On the other hand, I was of the philosophy that most actions in life were done in haste and the outcome would be okay or just "good enough." I was always in a hurry and hit the ground running each morning with the goal to finish my work and be on time for my boys after school. For most of my child-rearing years, daily plate spinning would be the norm, which is why I couldn't focus on writing. I did, however, keep reminders on snippets of paper, all sizes and shapes, where I had jotted down words, names and incidents. I also saved a mountain of newspaper articles, letters from inmates, and staff reports in a big, blue plastic bin marked DOC (Department of Corrections).

I moved from Minnesota to California in 2008 and moved three more times before opening the DOC bin in 2018. My plan when life settled down was to piece together ten years of what it was like to be a nurse in an all-male maximum-security prison in Stillwater, Minnesota. It was by far the best nursing job I ever had. I say that because the nursing we did covered every aspect of medicine except obstetrics and pediatrics. We functioned like nurses in a small town, with patients who had cancer, seizures, on dialysis, mental illness, trauma, communicable diseases and industrial accidents. We did triage, minor-surgery, orthopedics, and more, all in one place. With each patient's presentation, we had to learn quickly how to care for them or risk the chance of getting sued, which kept us up-to-date and well prepared for our next nursing positions outside the walls.

Today it is a well-known fact that the prison system in the US is broken. I witnessed this evolution from 1985-1995 where funding for Corrections went to warehousing and not rehabilitation; resulting in inmates spending a huge part of their lives in the revolving door of the prison system.

Most nurses will never see the inside of a prison except in the movies or television, but there are thousands of nurses working in

Corrections all over the US. Their dedication and care to men and women who are incarcerated brings some humanity back to those who could use a little hope. Nurses innately have that gift.

This is a book of my memories of my prison days, memories of staff, inmates and incidents all behind thick, metal bars, of a living, breathing subculture on 350 acres that was once a working farm.

The Flag:
Minnesota State Prison
Dining Hall Rules
June 1, 1909

1. On entering the dining hall take your seat promptly-position erect- arms folded, with eyes to the front until the signal is given to commence eating.

2. Strict silence must be observed during the meal. Staring at visitors, talking and laughing, fooling or gazing about the room is strictly forbidden.

3. Eating or drinking before or after the gong sounds, using vinegar in your drinking water or putting meat on a table is prohibited.

4. Should you desire additional food make your wants known to the waiters in the following manner:

   - If you want bread hold up your right hand.
   - Coffee or water, hold up your cup.
   - Meat, hold up your fork.
   - Soup, hold up your spoon.
   - Vegetables, hold up your knife.

If you desire to speak to an officer about food or service in the dining hall hold up your left hand.

5. Wasting food in any form will not be tolerated. You must not ask for or allow waiter to place on your plate more food than you can eat. When through with meal leave pieces of bread unmussed on left side of plate.

6. After finishing your meal place knife, fork and spoon on the right side of plate. Sit erect with arms folded. When the signal is given to arise drop hands to your side. At the second signal of the gong march out and to your respective places in line in a prompt, quiet and orderly manner.

7. In passing to and from the dining hall you must not gaze into cells or loiter on the gallery. Walk erect with your eyes to the front. It is against the rules to carry out any of the dining hall furnishings or to carry food to or from the dining hall at any time except on Sundays and holidays, when you will be allowed to carry lunch to your cell for the evening meal.

CONVICT LIFE IN THE MINNESOTA STATE PRISON, 1909

The Drugstore:
A Prelude to Prison

On slow nights Bill, the pharmacist and owner, would have me and other employees take a Q-tip dipped in alcohol and erase the word *Sample* from the pills he obviously received for free. We would ever so carefully hold the capsule with our thumb and forefinger and erase the word from each pill. We would then place the capsule back into the little brown prescription bottle. Hundreds of instances of the word *Sample* were erased during those otherwise idle times. Bill would place the tampered sample medication back on the shelf with the rest of the legitimately obtained medications until a prescription could make use of it. I don't recall being asked to wear gloves, or whether we were encouraged to even wash our hands. And I surely don't recall knowing what a federal offense was. But this simple criminal act, along with dusting the shelves of the store, were the two menial tasks that were to be done when we weren't waiting on customers. We were teenagers who most of the time did what we were told. Otherwise we were smoking cigarettes and dreaming. As far as we were concerned, the cigs were free—as was the Binaca to freshen our breath after the cigs, because we worked there. We were high school kids. What did we care? Our friends and our cigs were all that were important to us.

My drugstore attire was the same as my high school uniform because I was too lazy to walk the block home to change before starting my shift. I was wearing my Our Lady of Peace uniform consisting of a navy blue blazer with "OLP" sewn in gold on the left lapel. Also a white collared cotton blouse tucked into a navy blue straight skirt, hemmed to the knee: nuns' orders. Navy knee-high socks and navy oxfords completed the outfit. My oxfords were actually white saddle shoes dyed navy, because the holy store where my mother had to order all this Catholic cloth didn't carry my size 11 shoes. Mom and the owner of the Village Bootery put their heads together and figured out how to get a pair of uniform shoes on my feet without having to special-order them through the army, like she had to do for my brothers.

It was one of those slow nights where just Bill and I were standing at the long counter in the back of the pharmacy. Truthfully, on that particular night I was the only one standing and participating in the aforementioned federal offense. For some reason, dusting hadn't appealed to me that evening. Bill was watching a small TV he had discreetly hidden out of the customers' view. Some comedy show was blaring, because I remember Bill laughing along with the canned audience, and I remember thinking, *that's kind of loud. Must be his favorite show.* Bill wasn't a funny guy himself; or maybe he was with people his own age. He was short, bald, and had those bulging eyes like Marty Feldman in *Young Frankenstein.* He was constantly stressed and had a couple of little boys who would often come in and screw up the registers if we didn't catch them. Mostly he yelled a lot at all of us, including his wife; but apparently it was normal behavior for him, and his shouting didn't mean he disliked us, or so his wife said.

Still in my high school uniform and watching the slowest clock in St. Paul, I remember thinking I had learned a few things since I started working at the drugstore, two years ago. Only once had I yelled over the back counter, "Hey, Bill, where do you keep the Trojans?" I had looked everywhere before asking. Too bad for the customer that it was a busy Saturday morning and the place was packed, which was why I yelled in the first place. And I learned what a car's exhaust system was after I ran a prescription to Mrs. Rumsey's house. I was racing back down Marshall Avenue in Bill's Comet over the awesome bump where, as kids, we used to yell from the back seat, "Go faster!" when we saw it coming. I was flying. Unfortunately, the exhaust system was too—way behind me.

These are life lessons, I thought, as I stared at the clock that wasn't moving. Thank goodness it was 8:55. Only five more minutes and I would be off work and could head home to bed. I was beat.

But the tinkling from the front door bell startled me. In walked a customer. *One more sale*, I thought. I stood on my tiptoes to look over the shelves in front of me and down the aisles to see whom it was. *Hmmmm, that man doesn't look familiar.*

There were three aisles in the drugstore, all leading to the back two pharmacy counters. The lower counter was at the same height as the customers' waists and ran perpendicular to the three aisles. The second counter was twice as high and ran parallel to the first, separated only by a couple of feet with a single step. The pharmacist actually looked down on the customers from that counter.

It was at the second counter where I was standing when the 8:55 p.m. customer came in. *Something's weird about him*, I thought. He was already at the lower counter and I needed to get out there and wait on him…but I was hesitant. I looked at Bill, who was chortling away. *No help there.*

Slowly I started walking down to the end of the counter. *Quit it, scaredy-cat, what's your problem?* And still my oxfords felt like they were filled with cement. I paused, standing for a moment at the end of the counter, studying the new Tylenol display that blocked this man's face. He stood in front of the middle of the counter, where the old metal push-button cash register sat, waiting for me. My heart was beating so rapidly that my hands started trembling and I didn't know why. I took a very deep breath and sidestepped about a yard's length to the open counter space where he stood. Placing both hands on the counter to 1) hold myself up and 2) steady my shaking hands, I said, "Can I help you?" And then I saw it. His right hand slowly crept up from under the counter and the black tip of a metal cylinder was pointing at my belly. I had never seen a gun before, except in the movies, so I could only assume…but I was pretty sure it was real. Adding to the drama: the man was wearing surgical gloves with powder in them. I never looked up at his face, or I don't think I did; he replied, "Empty the register," as he shoved a pillowcase toward me. All I could think of was, *this guy doesn't know Bill is in the back watching TV. Should I tell him?* No words came out, though, or I should say that words came out of me but didn't make sense to the robber; he seemed agitated with my putziness. Finally, the word *Bill* and my head jerking frantically to the right as though I was having a grand mal seizure was what he understood. The robber said, "Get him out here."

"Bill," I said, raising my voice a bit. "Bill," I repeated, a little louder.

No answer.

"Bill!" I yelled.

"Ye-e-e-s-s, coming," he replied nonchalantly. I could hear movement.

Bill had been through several robberies and always told us if it happened to us we were just to do whatever we were asked to do by the robber, the money didn't matter.

Bill came from the back and stood next to me, his belly now in the gun's line of fire. I stepped to the right. "Empty it," the robber said.

And so Bill did, but not before I suddenly came back to life and asked if he wanted the checks. Being new at this, I didn't know if checks had value to robbers, and also I had hidden the big bills under the checks, so if he said "no," he wouldn't get the twenties or fifties. In fact, he shouted *"No!"* and again appeared agitated with me. Bill continued to pull the bills out from each of their rows and I, hoping to speed things up, inquired again, "Do you want the change?"

"No!" he shouted once more.

Whew! I thought. *No change, no checks. This should go fast and I can go home.*

Bill closed the register and handed the pillowcase back to the robber. He waved the gun and said, "Get in the back."

Oh no, here we go. What next?

I wasn't that good a Catholic but I was praying the Hail Mary with the utmost sincerity. Bill turned to walk to the back counter but he slowed up as he climbed the step, which slowed me down, as I was like Velcro on Bill's back, which placed the robber's gun into the small of my back. Then I heard the crabby robber's command, "Keep moving."

The three of us were now in the back of the pharmacy and I was still breathing and much more alert now that the attention was on Bill. I decided to stand in front of the safe, which was housed under the counter, where I figured my large-sized saddle shoes might block the robber's vision. He didn't seem to notice the safe or me, and frankly I wasn't looking at him either. I stared at his shoes. He was telling Bill to give him all the Class A narcotics and to place them in the pillowcase. And Bill did what he was told while I continued to stare at the robber's feet. Next, the robber told us to lie on the floor. I was in a skirt, so I aimed my backside away from Bill and knelt down on my knees. I lay on my belly with my head on my crossed arms looking up at Bill. Bill was lying down and facing me, only he was covering the back of his head with his hands. *Oh no,* I thought in a panic. *Bill thinks he is going to be shot in the back of the head! How much more drama can I take?* The robber was standing by the step leading to the lower counter when he started his exit speech: "Sorry I have to do this and you won't get hurt if—"

And then the tinkling of the front door bells sounded.

Alerted by the bells, the robber turned toward the front door and said, "Don't move."

Move? Not on your life, buddy, I assured him in my head.

The robber left us for a moment, pursuing the poor guy who was shopping in the front of the store. There was no time for Bill and me to have a chat—they were back. It was none other than my friend Bernie, who was being escorted toward the counters with the gun to his back. Bernie would sometimes stop by when I was working...to steal something. This time he was holding a yellow Hi-Lighter, as he was attending the University of Minnesota and needed it for class, apparently. He was told to lie down beside Bill and me. Bernie was an old hockey player and was raised in the notoriously tough West Seventh Street neighborhood, where fighting was the norm. As he was adjusting himself into his lying-down position next to me and Bill, who was still covering his head, he whispered, "For two cents I'd deck this guy." The robber, still pointing his gun at us, started his exit speech again: "Really sorry I had to do this but—"

Once again the front door's tinkling bells interrupted him.

This time it was a nerd, a student who was attending St. Thomas College down the street. He, too, needed a yellow highlighter apparently. The nerd also had a lot of opinions for this robber, like, "Don't worry about me man, if you take the freeway you'll be way ahead of the cops." Or "You don't have to worry about me cuz I won't call the cops." But the robber was too agitated to care about his nervous chatter and simply told him to "Shut up and lie down."

Finally, the four of us, two by two, face-to-face, listened to what I hoped was the last exit speech.

"Really sorry I had to do this," the robber told us, "and you won't get hurt if you don't move until I drive away. And if you move you will get hurt, I promise you."

And then he left.

The four of us were silent and did not move until we heard the welcome melody of the front door's tinkly bells informing us the door had closed. Then Bill took his hands down from the back of his head and slowly crept up off his belly and onto his knees. Not standing yet he reached up, stretching his right arm up toward the top of the shelf where the phone hung, so he could call the police. On my belly and not moving (as instructed), I listened for the car motor going past the front door, so I would know the robber had left our neighborhood. At the same time Bill, still on both knees but with

15

the phone to his ear, pulled out his keys to the front door. He tossed them down to me. "Go lock the front door," he said.

Was he kidding? *No way am I moving.... You heard the guy!*

Out loud I said, desperately, "Bill, he hasn't gone by yet. Wait till he drives by."

Finally we heard the car that had been idling alongside the store pull away. I ran down the side aisle to the front door, crouching a bit when I was directly in front of the glass door, just in case. Then I quickly locked it and ran back to the safety of the back counter. I glanced up at the slowest clock in St. Paul. It was only 9:08 p.m.

The police arrived shortly thereafter and everyone but me left the back counter. I needed it for support for my trembling body. My mother heard the sirens and could see the squad cars surrounding the drugstore from the front door of our home. She became alarmed, knowing that I was working, and sent a couple of my older brothers down to see what was up. One policeman had begun interviewing Bill, and the nerdy guy was giving an extensive recounting of the incident—including a detailed description of the robber—to another policeman. Bernie was back in the far aisle, stealing. Then all of a sudden two more policemen ran into the store, saying, "What kind of shoes did he have on? We just picked up a guy on Selby Avenue. Can you describe his shoes?"

Everyone was silent.

We turned to look at each other while waiting for someone—*anyone*—to respond. No one said anything.

Finally, I found my voice. I rose up on my tiptoes and popped my head over the back counter. "White, dirty, Converse high-tops!" I yelled.

"Call it in," one officer said to the other. "We got our guy."

This was my first and only robbery where a gun was used.

The second time we were robbed I didn't even know it was happening until a customer waiting in line waved Bill over to say that he thought he saw a woman put her hand in the register drawer while I had stepped away for a few seconds. I had been picking up a product for another customer standing at the end of the counter: a man who refused to come closer to the register and wanted to buy only products that were on the bottom shelf behind me. This was after I had rung up his purchase and was ready to close him out; he changed his mind and insisted that I show him something else behind me. If I had closed the register drawer the other purchases I had rung up would have disappeared and I would have had to start over again. On that busy Saturday morning, that wasn't an option. While I stepped away, I still had my right hand on the open drawer. A woman waiting at the counter on the opposite side of the register placed her hand into the drawer and in one quick motion pulled out dollar bills then quickly walked out the door. That was what the alert customer had told Bill.

Immediately, Bill came to the register and closed it out like he did each night. Based on his calculations he quickly deduced that we had been robbed. The police were called, statements were taken, and a few days later a policeman arrived to show me mug shots. All the full-face headshots triggered no recognition on my part, but once I saw the side views I picked out the accomplice to the woman who robbed us. This led us to court, where the accomplice (now inmate) was finally caught robbing a liquor store. When the prosecuting attorney asked each of us if the man sitting at the next table with his attorney was the man in our drugstore, I was the only one who said yes. Other employees could identify the woman but not the man.

Fifteen years later that same inmate stood in front of me for a blood pressure check. We had made a note in his chart that he shouldn't get Sudafed due to his high blood pressure—and he was asking for Sudafed. I had recognized him immediately when I started working at the prison, but he didn't remember me. I wondered how I would have responded had he put two and two together. After all, I pointed directly at him in court when asked if the man who lured me away from the cash register was sitting in court. "Yes, your honor," I had said, "sitting right there."

Neither I, nor he, knew that we would meet again behind bars.

Claustrophobia

During my job interview the head nurse met me in the front of the prison and, after going through two secured areas and my receiving a visitor's tag, she walked me down a long flagstone hallway where I passed four large cell halls. Each cell hall, she said, housed about 200 inmates on four tiers (levels). The top tier was enclosed with fencing. I realized later that if an inmate jumped or was pushed over the top tier, the result would be instant death, so I could understand the fencing, but on the lower tiers, if one jumped or were pushed, the results would be massive internal injuries and broken bones.

I remember asking her where all the nurses were and she replied, "Oh, all over, I guess." We stopped halfway down the hall and entered another barred door, where we were, this time, buzzed in by a guard sitting in a large, raised booth not enclosed in glass but in fencing. Once inside, we were standing in another enclosed area with benches attached to the walls. Here, new inmates waited to get their IDs and others waited to be escorted up to Health Services on scheduled runs.

This place was called the "security center." Here the two captains had their offices. This is where all the "counting" of the inmates went on. This was also the shift command center. The guard on the other side of the door unlocked it and we walked through.

Now we had a choice of four doors. We moved to the second to the last door on the left and the same guard opened that door as well. The head nurse said we were going to the "quiet cells," whatever that meant. I followed behind, not intimidated yet.

On my right was a row of small cells, cave-like, with very thick doors—four of them that the nurse called "condemned cells." Here unruly inmates did some "quiet" time for their misbehavior. These cells hadn't been used for many years but she wanted me to see the inside of them. We had to duck our heads to enter the small, cramped, cement cavern, only to go through yet another door deeper into the cell the size of a large dog kennel. We were in pitch-blackness and I was praying she didn't shut the first door. Being claustrophobic, I didn't want to start clawing at the walls during my interview. I held my panic at bay and she explained that these cells were closed because of lawsuits by inmates. I had seen enough prison movies to know that these cells were called "the hole." I could see why the inmates had sued: to do time in one of these cells was a punishment beyond belief.

The head nurse didn't scare me away and in May 1985 she hired me for a temporary position working the graveyard shift.

A few months into my new prison nurse career, I got a call from my sister that a good friend of ours had been abducted. After recovering from her ordeal, our friend Ann was able to describe in detail her harrowing experience.

Ann worked in downtown St. Paul, Minnesota, and daily parked her car in the contract-parking structure next door. Leaving work at four-fifteen p.m., she described the day as beautiful while she climbed the eight flights to the level where her car was parked. She had been parking in this same space for several months because it had large ceiling lights and was closest to the outside where there was daylight. She recalls there were no cars parked between the stairway door and her car and only noticed how bright the sunshine was and that there was no one around.

After unlocking her car door, she put the key in the ignition but didn't relock her door. She turned to get the parking ticket out of her purse when suddenly a man was in her car, his face very close to hers, telling her to "Move over, I want your car." At first she thought, as many women do, that it was a joke. She responded, "What?" very confused. He said again, "I want your car," but this time he raised his left hand, which held a knife.

Ann began to scream, "No, no, no" and backed away while the man put his hand over her mouth and pushed her down across the seat, wedging her head against the passenger door. He said, "Shut up, shut up and you won't get hurt." She recalls that despite his words, his face and the knife, what she heard was, "I'm going to rape you."

She stopped screaming and couldn't breathe as he took his hand away. He sat up in the driver's seat and told her to sit up and look out the window and ordered, "Don't look at me." Ann did what he said while struggling to breathe. Next he pulled Ann's arms behind her back and tied her wrists with a piece of fabric. Ann recalls starting to lean back against the passenger seat when the man brutally pushed her head against the window and said, "Don't look at me" once more. She remembers a long pause where she broke the silence by saying, "What are you going to do?" He did not respond. Another long pause. She said, "If you are going to take the car, what do you need me for?" Again he did not respond. Next the man turned the key in the ignition but the car did not start. Ann later explained to us that it was a diesel and you had to open the choke and wait for the glow plug before starting the car; this was something the man didn't know. He tried again and said, "Why won't it start?" Ann replied, "I don't know," while still staring out the window but sneaking glimpses over her shoulder of the side of his face, shoulder and hand.

Eventually the man got the car started and attempted to exit the parking structure, but because this building was old and there were no exit signs or a spiral ramp to go down, you had to exit by going down each level following the faded arrows painted on the incline ramps. The man was confused and preceded to go down one ramp, but turned into an adjacent ramp, then backing up, turning around only to go down the up ramp. And the whole time Ann was hoping someone would notice his erratic driving but there was no one around.

After some time he stopped on the seventh level, pulling into a parking space where he rested his arms on the steering wheel and muttered, "Sure, steal a car," and mumbled some more. He turned to Ann and said, "What will it cost to get out of here?" Ann said she didn't know, even though she knew it would cost $7.50 for a lost ticket. The man took Ann's purse and looked for her wallet where she knew she only had a dollar or two. Ann went on to say, "It won't work, and you won't be able to get out of the ramp. I've parked here for years, they know me, and they know the car. They'll stop you. Why don't you just leave?" When actually Ann knew that the ramp attendant was new and had only been on the job a week. Next the man asked, "Where is the ticket?" Ann replied, "I don't know." He took everything out of her purse, many receipts and papers, and eventually found the ticket. Ann said, "If you hand in that ticket they will say, where is Ann? I've signed it. It won't work."

Suddenly he got out of the car, went to the back and put the key in the trunk but it would not open. He tried again and again until finally he turned the key the opposite way and the trunk opened.

Ann watched him from the rearview mirror and noticed his base-ball cap but could not make out the letters. The man returned to the driver's seat and leaned over and unlocked the passenger door. He got out and walked over to her door, opened it saying, "Get out." Ann turned to him and placed both feet on the ground and said, "No." There was a long pause and a stare down and he said, "Get out." Ann distinctly remembers thinking that "if I live I am going to identify you." She wanted to remember everything. She finally said, "I won't get out until you tell me what you're going to do."

He reached into his pocket and pulled the knife back out and opened it saying, "I didn't think I'd have to do this." Ann immediately stood up and the man picked her up by the waist and placed her in the trunk. She did not resist. Still there was no one around.

The man started the car, backed out of the space and again drove erratically, backing up to turn down on some of the up ramps. Ann was waiting for him to get to the front gate. She realized later that with all the confusion of stopping and starting, she missed when he exited the ramp. He turned on the radio loudly and Ann heard the announcer say it was four thirty-five as he weaved through down-town St. Paul. Ann positioned herself into the innermost corner of the trunk to prevent being tossed around by the man's poor driving skills. She felt he was going to cause an accident, which she hoped for, so it would stop the car.

Ann started losing track of where the man was going. She became lethargic, almost sleepy, and started considering several things: no one would be looking for her although she was expected home; her sons would not be worried if she was late; she had prom-ised pizza for dinner. She was certain she would be raped and was wondering if she would be stabbed, wondering what that would feel like. She wondered if she was getting carbon monoxide poisoning coming from the exhaust and if she would get brain damage from it. She worried about the terrible shock this would be to her husband and children and suddenly the pain in her right shoulder and arm woke her up. She had completely forgotten that her hands were tied behind her back and hadn't tried to free them. She changed positions and began to work frantically to get the material to move but got nowhere. She calmed down and began to pull her wrists rhythmically up and down inside the fabric. She said she knew if she did this systematically it would work.

While working on her restraints, she felt the car stop. Ann heard the man say, "There is no gas." She then heard a response. Was a second person in the car? Or he could have been talking to himself, she didn't know.

Ann got her hands free and became very excited. This was the first time she could take some action and get some control back. She said she had no idea what would happen but felt she could put up a fight, as she knew there were tools in her trunk. When she moved to the rear end of the trunk, she could see a red glow from the taillights through the access panel. She put her eye up to the panel and she could see electrical wires. Her idea was to get a tool and somehow disconnect the wires to the taillights in hopes that the man would be pulled over by the police for no taillights. But it was only five p.m. and the sun was still shining. Suddenly it dawned on her after poking her fingers around the panels... the trunk lock! She could picture the latch mechanism from the hundreds of times she had opened the trunk. By now she knew they were on a freeway. She began visualizing how the lock worked and knew it was some kind of spring. She poked her fingers into every opening she could find. She realized she was too high in the hood panels and found holes closer to the floor. Finally her index finger found something. She knew this was the trunk latch. She pushed her finger into the hole to get behind it but couldn't get it to move. Her plan was to figure out how the latch worked; then, when the car stopped, she would pop the latch and run before he could get out of the car. Ann pulled harder and harder on the latch when suddenly the trunk hood flew up!

Ann saw heavy traffic with many cars very close to her car. She was kneeling now up against the back of the trunk for stability and frantically waving and screaming, "Help me, help me, police, police!" She knew the drivers couldn't hear her and she couldn't see their faces but she kept at it for what seemed like forever, until the man saw what she was doing and started exiting the freeway. Several cars were following behind as they moved into the exit lane. They remained a good distance back from her car. Ann had no intention of jumping out of the trunk because she had felt safe while the cars were following her, but now the cars started dwindling to two or three. Therefore she made a decision to jump while the man reached the exit ramp. She calculated the slowest the car would go up the exit and was pretty sure the cars behind her would not run her over. She placed one leg out over the back of the trunk.

Her foot never touched the ground. The momentum of the car pulled her forward and she landed on her face on the pavement. Ann clearly recalls the pavement coming up to her face and then she was on her back; she thinks she bounced. She got up off the pavement and walked a few feet to the grass and lay down. The driver of the car behind her stopped and immediately came to help her. Ann thinks that someone with a CB (Citizens Band) radio on the freeway called 911, because an ambulance arrived and she was taken to United Hospital in downtown St. Paul. Once in the hospital, she asked a nurse if she could use the phone to call home. Her ten-year-old son picked up and she explained that she had been in an accident but was okay; however, the car was not okay but there was no reason to worry. Her son listened intently and replied, "Okay, Mom, but can we still have pizza for dinner?"

The man was caught, sentenced and brought to Stillwater Prison. I made sure that all my guard-friends knew who he was and what he had done to Ann. They took it from there. I finally met the man, now inmate, after his leg got pretty scraped up in a softball game. I vigorously scrubbed the dirt out of the wound as hard as I could. I lathered up the leg with an antiseptic that would surely burn, knowing that the little pain I was causing him was nothing compared to the lifelong scar he inflicted on Ann.

That was thirty-three years ago and, sadly, the 2018 Brett Kavanaugh Supreme Court hearings brought back Ann's painful memories of her abduction. She too remembered his hand over her mouth and his body on top of hers, similar to what Dr. Christine Blasey Ford testified. That memory will be forever frozen in her brain.

Ann is every woman's hero, a 110-pound, petite, powerful force. A woman who would not back down, memorizing every detail while staring into the face of her abductor because in her mind, if she lived, by identifying him in a lineup, she would send him to prison.

The man did his time and was let out of prison only to rape and rob his next victim(s) for the next twenty years. He has been in and out of prison until the present, and will not be eligible to be released until he is well into his eighties.

This man is pure evil, a minority in the prison population. My only wish is that they would reopen those condemned cells and let the man feel what it's like to be traumatized in an enclosed space, like the trunk of a car.

Night Shift

For the first six months of my correctional career I worked the graveyard shift, 11:30 p.m.-7:00 a.m. I wasn't opposed to starting on the lowest rung of the ladder but I was determined to advance my shift into the daylight hours. Coming into the prison at night was dark and eerily quiet. I knew hundreds of men were settling down or already sleeping, yet I couldn't see any movement in the darkened cell halls. There was only one officer sitting in each of the four cell halls with a solitary light over the paperwork on his desk. Passing the halls, I would arrive outside the Security Center (the command post of the prison), where the officer would have to stop what he was doing and escort me to the side door. Here he would unlock the door and announce over the radio to the Health Services officer that I was on my way up. There was a bright light outside the side door that guided me between buildings, but because this prison was in Minnesota, I sometimes had to deal with the elements like extreme snow or rain. Snow on the prison compound was dealt with immediately. There was a crew of inmates who kept all walkways cleared using snow shovels. These inmates were let out of their cells sometimes very early in the morning to shovel before the day shift arrived.

About a block away and up a flight of steps, the next officer was waiting for me so he could unlock the Health Services front door. All security procedures on this shift were muted but secure: no ᴜud talking in person or over the radios; after all, there were 1400 men and one nurse trying to sleep.

Upon arriving at the nursing office, my first priority was checking the ward to make sure all inmates admitted were okay and didn't need anything or, if they did, I'd give them the needed attention so they would settle down for the night. Next, I would start cleaning the exam rooms, restocking shelves emptied of ace bandages and gauze pads and whatever else was used during the day. Lastly, I would refill all the diabetic insulin boxes with fresh sterile syringes and the appropriate insulin for each inmate according to the doctor's orders. This would take me to about 1:30 a.m. Now what?

Each night was a battle trying to stay awake. Once in awhile there would be a call from the guards that they were bringing an inmate up who was having trouble breathing. Usually this was not a heart attack but a panic attack from a new inmate, who didn't know he was claustrophobic until his cell door closed and locked behind him. I started bringing in brown paper lunch bags and I would teach these inmates how to breathe slowly into the bag every time they felt an attack coming on. At least for the six months that I was on the night shift, panic attacks were about all I saw.

Staying awake was the hardest part of the shift. The officers had to strictly adhere to the stay-awake policy or be written up if they were caught sleeping. I didn't worry much, although I always asked when I arrived whom the officer assigned to the hospital was. Some were hyper-vigilant and strict rule followers, others were not. One time the regular night nurse woke the guard to inform him that while making her rounds in the ward, she had noticed that the bars over the window in the bathroom were being sawed apart. He was awarded "Officer of the Month" for foiling an attempted escape, even though the bathroom window only led to the outside of the Health Services building, still inside the prison compound.

A good night for me was at least four to five hours of sleep. I would actually be depressed if I only got a couple of hours. Little did anyone know I was still nursing my six-month-old baby boy and also at home were his two brothers, ages twenty-one months and four years; sleep was past history, and I was beyond exhausted.

After all my tasks were finished, I would sit at the desk in the nursing office with the officer outside my door and I would try everything in my power to keep my forehead from slamming onto the desk. My arms would go numb holding my head and I would go a little crazy popping up to every sound, no matter how small. So I figured out a different system. My boldness grew from my exhaustion and I would matter-of-factly tell the guard exactly what time to wake me up, like he was my personal alarm clock. Then I would curl up on the EKG table with a blanket and pillow and trust that the guard would come and get me at the correct time -- or worse, if he got a call over the radio that the Watch Lieutenant was on his way up for a visit.

Some of these officers chose the night shift to avoid the prison bureaucracy, but others, had a full-time day job, like "Big Lou," who was a grade school teacher. Another, a night Watch Lieutenant, was literally and figuratively a clown. His stage name was Giggles and he always had free circus tickets for my kids.

Years later, Giggles and I were on the day shift and we were assigned to drive an inmate home to die. Bill was terminally ill with cancer. Medically speaking, we guessed he had only a few days to live. Bill had sexually abused his daughter while being a raging drunk and while in prison worked his AA program. His wife, a nurse, wanted him to die at home.

I was at a meeting at the Department of Corrections where the Commissioner had his office and decided to drop in on him to let him know first hand about Bill's declining health. What I told the Commissioner was that we were taking care of two dying inmates in the ward, one in for sexual assault and one doing time for murder. The one in for murder was on his deathbed but still had the energy to be arrogant and nasty to his family and us, while the other, Bill was silently and peacefully making amends for his crime. The Commissioner came to the prison and interviewed both inmates; he decided to let Bill go home and, except for doctor's appointments, Bill could not leave the house. Giggles and I dropped Bill off at his unlocked house in Rochester, Minnesota, where we heard he lived for another six weeks. Under hospice care, the other inmate eventually died surrounded by some of his closest cellmates. After our doctor pronounced him dead and his friends left the area, we washed him up and waited for the officer to come back with the security protocol for a deceased inmate.

It was both interesting and ludicrous to me; after watching this inmate die and physically having to wash his lifeless body, the death protocol was that he had to have his hands and feet handcuffed to the gurney. Not only was his dead body not going anywhere but I was assigned to sit and stare at him until the coroner picked him up to make sure he was, in fact, still dead.

My night shift days finally came to an end when, unexpectedly, the full time evening nurse gave her notice and I went from part time to full time with benefits. Starting my shift in the daylight and ending in the dark was like winning the lottery for me the exhausted nurse and mother of three.

Segregation

The segregation unit was the jail within the prison where up to 100 inmates lived, some for a year because of an escape and some for infractions committed while in prison. Of the four levels, the top tier was saved for Federal inmates housed there during their court hearings. A few famous Wounded Knee offenders and Minnesota's drug king, Ralph Chavous "Plukey" Duke, were housed on that top tier. Unfortunately, it was also a unit that many times housed the mentally ill because of some sort of acting out. And yes, if any bodily fluids were thrown at staff, it would be from a "seg" cell.

Some of the mentally ill inmates became almost permanent residents in seg and the staff would put them to work, menial jobs like polishing the flagstone floors by hand. One inmate spent so much time in seg that he learned to mimic the guards talking to each other on their radios. He did this by placing his mouth in the crook of his bent elbow. There were times where I would be on the tiers with an officer and I would hear some insane order over the guard's radio, only to find out that the command was coming from a few cells down the tier by Simon, the prison's craziest inmate. This, of course, sent me into peals of laughter, as I couldn't believe how he perfectly imitated the officer's radio chats. Simon would make noise like static first by blowing a swishing-type sound into his bent arm and then he'd perfectly imitate a guard's voice issuing a command like, "*Code*

3 Seg." It became so common that in future radio banter I had to ask the guard if it was real or Simon. Funny, I heard stories from officers escorting Simon to court hearings where he acted as sane as the judge sentencing him, but in prison, his home, he could act worse than a toddler on his worst day. And yes, Simon was famous for throwing his bodily fluids at staff too.

While making my rounds one day, I came upon a couple of creative inmates who were playing a game of chess. Not on a table and not using a game with board pieces, but sitting on their cell floors, one sitting below his bars in the far left corner of his cell and his neighbor sitting on his floor at the far right corner of his cell. Out on the tier floor, between the two cells, was a makeshift board made out of cardboard. The chess pieces were fashioned from the inmates' cereal boxes, toilet paper, or the cardboard from the toilet paper roll or any other piece of paper-type material that came into their cells, then wetting the paper (a poor man's paper-mâché), shaping the game figures into kings, chessmen, pawns or checker pieces, and they had a game of chess or checkers. The inmates saved everything that came into their seg cell for future use, which at the time I thought was genius.

There were three cells on the "flag" (ground level) when you first came into the seg unit. One was a quiet cell with a big, heavy, steel door with a slot mid-door to pass a meal tray through. The others were like regular cells but with the water turned off. Inmates who were suicidal or suspected of swallowing a balloon full of drugs were housed there. Balloons were commonly passed in the visiting room where inmates and their girlfriends were allowed to kiss. But if an inmate quickly walked to the vending machine to buy a soda after making out with his gal, the officers would become suspicious that a balloon had been passed. The officer would then arrest the inmate, ban the girlfriend, or call the local police to come and arrest her and bring the inmate to the first cell in the seg unit until the balloon was passed. No flushing in that cell, and because there was a guard directly across from the cell in the control booth, he would be able to see if the inmate was using the toilet. Those cells not only didn't have water turned on, they also did not give the inmate a blanket or pillow, just a bare mattress. The dress code in that cell was a tent-like dress made out of heavy-duty cloth. Smaller inmates could literally curl up inside the dress and keep warm in the huge ball of material.

Some violent inmates would be placed in the quiet cell for disruptive behavior like harming themselves by cutting or cigarette burns, or attacking others. These inmates were allowed to have the water on and wore the tent-like dress over their naked bodies. One mentally ill inmate read a passage in his bible, Matthew 18:9, stating: "If your eye causes you to stumble, pluck it out…." We caught him before he actually "plucked" his eye out and sent him to the hospital to salvage what was left of his vision, before returning him to the quiet cell.

Others were so physically violent that they were four-point restrained, face down on a board. This is where the nurses came in. Every shift one of us would go to that seg cell to make sure the inmate was okay, not happy but medically okay. As the naked inmate was lying face down, the officer would cover his buttocks with a towel, and then we would kneel down next to the board and speak to the inmate. We would make sure that he had good blood flow to all extremities and try to convince him to cooperate with the seg staff so that he could be, first, released from the board and, secondly, be able to return to his cell.

One Cuban inmate named Mario was placed in the quiet cell. He was on a hunger strike, feeling he was mistreated, and he decided he was going to cut himself so deeply in the femoral artery of his thigh that he would show those guards and bleed to death. The officers in his cell hall saw what he was doing and took all sharp objects away from him by placing him in the segregation unit, where we nurses checked on him every shift. When it was my turn to check on him, he looked to make sure no guards were watching and subtly, he slowly opened his mouth and moved a very small piece of glass, less than an inch long, to the tip of his tongue. This was the tool he was using to dissect through the layers of thigh tissue to get to the artery. Then he pulled his tent dress up his thigh and revealed a wound so deep that I could see his artery pulsating. So what was he thinking? If he sliced his artery, he would bleed to death in a matter of minutes and he would die. He was Cuban from the Mariel BoatLift; we had at least 60 of these Marielitos in prison. I couldn't understand his thought process, nor did I report him to the guards regarding the hidden glass in his cheek. I knew that if I told the guards about the tiny piece of glass, they would blitz him to try to get it out of his mouth and he would swallow it. Next he would be sent to the hospital because of the possibility of bleeding internally, or if he fought the guards and they got the piece of glass, they would four-point restrain him, face down on the board, as an active suicidal risk and I knew the situation would only get worse from there. So for the next couple of days, every time I checked on him he would click that tiny piece of glass to his front teeth to prove to me that he was winning his solo game against the guards. He eventually got tired of the tent dress and his cold, barren environment and was returned to his cell, femoral artery intact.

At some point in the 1990s, all the Cuban inmates were sent back to Florida. There was one squirrelly little guy I was especially glad to see go. Every time I was on his tier, he would start bouncing on his bunk, flapping his arms up and down doing jumping jacks, completely naked.

Every once in a while when I made my rounds in seg, there would be a guard working the control booth who would play music for the inmates, speakers loudly reverberating throughout the entire stone-steel cell block. Often the seg guards and inmates sang like rock stars to their favorite tunes. One was *We Gotta Get Out of This Place* by The Animals.

Not every day was horrible in seg. I could see why Simon made it his home.

Tier 2:

Quiet cells (left side), the segregation unit at Stillwater State Prison (2007). *Photo obtained with permission from MediaNews Group/St. Paul Pioneer Press via Getty Images.*

Rudy

Everyone knew Rudy—everyone in law enforcement, that is. They knew him at the Minneapolis police department and the Hennepin County jail. But Stillwater Prison was where he lived most of the time; otherwise, he was homeless.

He was a happy-go-lucky, slap-you-on-the-back, drug-induced, mentally ill type guy. Tall and gangly thin, always disheveled-looking. Sauntered about like "Goofy," Disney's anthropomorphic dog character. He barely had a working tooth in his head, but that didn't stop him from constantly grinning.

Hanging in the Health Services building was a poster, "This is your brain on drugs," showing two scrambled eggs in a frying pan. That was Rudy's brain, all right. But despite the shape of his brain, everyone liked him.

In prison, Rudy was required to come to the Health Services building twice a day. He took a handful of different psych medications to keep him in the here-and-now. And some pills were for the side effects created by the here-and-now pills. He was required to open his mouth after swallowing to show the nurse that he indeed had swallowed all the pills. One spring day Rudy was particularly happy upon entering the Health Services building and I noticed he greeted the guard like they were a couple of kindred spirits. As he proceeded to the pill window where I was holding his pills and water cup, he leaned further toward me than usual and instinct told me that he was going to try to kiss me.

With a forearm block I stopped the attempted kiss and probably stunned Rudy back into reality, as he next found himself in the segregation unit written up for "inappropriate behavior toward a nurse," which carried a thirty-day sentence. Not a good place to be, as segregation is the jail in the prison. No TV, no radio, no exercise, no fun—but there was Rudy, yucking it up with his homies.

Each day the nurses would make several trips to the segregation unit to dispense pills or some kind of treatment. This cell hall was set with four tiers, all enmeshed with wire fencing to deter any jumpers. It held one hundred inmates, twenty-five on each tier. The nurse, along with a guard, would walk the tiers cell by cell, bar by bar, and find the inmate/patient in need of his medication.

And so it began. Every time I was assigned to "seg" rounds, I would cut through the side door and, once inside, the guard in the "sally port" would buzz me into the segregation unit itself. The heavy steel door would start sliding open as the guard pushed the buzzer and it would make a horrible metal-on-metal clanking clanging noise similar to a slow- moving train. This door-opening procedure would often wake the hundred inmates, who mostly slept the day away. As the door would slide open, the roar of a hundred male voices would start the chant, "Rudy, your girlfriend is here. Rudy, your girlfriend is here." That roar always reminded me of what the Beatles probably heard as they stepped on stage. In the cement and iron cell hall, the yelling reverberated off the brick walls and if I didn't know better, I might have thought I was stepping into a riot. On the third tier I'd find Rudy, standing at the bars with his arms hanging through them, ready to shake hands with anyone walking by. The same old goofy Rudy, grinning with his Billy-Bob teeth, so proud to have a girlfriend.

That was in 1995. On October 31, 1997, the Minneapolis Tribune headlined a story:

Police say man died aiding 2 rape victims. Father thinks son likely used boxing skills to do right thing. Staff writer Ka Vang wrote: *Rudy Tori Pacheco, Jr. wanted to grow up to be a boxer like his father, twice a Golden Glove champion in the late 1950's and early '60's. Instead the 41-year-old Pacheco, diagnosed with mental illness at age 16, roamed the streets of the Twin Cities until Tuesday night. Just before midnight, he stumbled upon a gruesome gang rape, tried to do the right thing and paid for it with his life, police told the family. Police say Pacheco and two other homeless men were looking for a place to sleep when they started toward the abandoned debris-filled, rat-infested grain elevator on Ninth Avenue and Second Street near downtown Minneapolis. Inside, the three came upon three other men raping and beating two women, police told the family. Authorities told Rudy's father, Rudy Pacheco, Sr., that his son and the other two men tried to intervene but were viciously beaten by the women's attackers. Pacheco's lifeless body eventually ended up at the bottom of an elevator shaft, having fallen three floors. Police say he suffered massive head injuries and his neck had been slashed. "He was homeless and an alcoholic, but he had a good heart," the elder Pacheco said. "My son really liked boxing. It was the only thing he could do well. I am sure he was using his boxing skills to protect himself and others." The intervention may have saved others' lives. The attackers were distracted long enough for one of the assaulted women to escape, leaving a trail of blood from the abandoned building to a nearby payphone on Washington Ave. where she dialed 9-1-1. Late Wednesday a bloody handprint on a pole near the phone was still visible, as were pools of blood in the parking lot of a nearby gas station.... Police said that debris inside the building made investigating the crime difficult. Any of the debris could have been used as a weapon.... The condition also made rescuing the victims difficult. Firefighters had to pluck Pacheco and the injured from the building with aerial equipment because of the debris, rats and lack of light. Rudy Pacheco, Sr. said, "It doesn't surprise me one bit that Rudy died trying to help someone. He was a good boy."*

PTSD
Post-Traumatic Stress Disorder

Not all nurses have nerves of steel. There are times when a nursing situation can become mentally unnerving. For example, while in nursing school I was assigned to a scoliosis patient, a teenage girl who had had her surgery to correct curvature of the spine and now was placed in a halo cast. This cast was not the type of cast made from plaster. This was a large metal ring around the forehead connected at four points to metal rods, two in the front and two in the back of the head that then connected to a stiff vest surrounding the body. The metal rods were attached to the metal ring with so-called "pins." From my point of view the metal pins should have been renamed "screws" because that's what they looked like and functioned as. They were drilled into the patient's skull in order for the whole contraption to stabilize the neck and head. My nursing instructor assured me that the patient's head was numbed before the doctor drilled the four holes into her head, but that explanation didn't eliminate my panic about seeing the screws drilled into the head-holes. It seemed so barbaric to me that I worried about it to the point where I was going to ask the nursing instructor to give me a patient without the halo cast, but I didn't.

With a pounding heart I stood outside the patient's room and knocked a couple of times before slowly opening her door. Her curtain was pulled around her bed I couldn't see her. I said, "Hello, Janie, I'm your student nurse Ellen. How are you doing?" She replied, "Great, just had a bath. Come in." I slowly took a deep breath and tentatively pulled the curtain back to find a young girl lying in her bed without the halo cast on. I was so relieved I could have cried. The holes in her head were not prominent and I was able to carry on my student-nurse tasks.

Fast forward to working the day shift at the prison. During the week several nurses were on duty and if there was a medical code, two of us would take off running to the unknown emergency. Having another nurse with me kept me calm and even if the code happened to be an inmate being thrown off a tier, I'm pretty sure I could have handled it. But on the weekends there was only one nurse per shift and my panic started festering. Not worried about stabbings, fights, broken bones, heart attacks, or even hangings, my anxiety was about being alone on a code where an inmate was tossed over the railings from the highest tier. I was sure he would land on his skull, which on impact would bust open, exposing his brains on the flagstone floor. I had heard stories that some pushed inmates landed on their feet like a cat, only to break their ankle bones, but I knew that, with my luck, the inmate I would have to deal with would land on his head.

One Saturday morning I arrived for my shift only to find out that I wasn't on the schedule. I had assumed it was my weekend, but another nurse, Greg, was there in my place. I was elated, it was 7 a.m. and I couldn't get out of the prison fast enough and back to bed. Greg was a super-nice, sensitive man, married with young children, working part time at the prison to try to make ends meet.

Unbeknownst to Greg, that afternoon, a Code 3 medical in the recreation yard would later be called. One of the Cuban inmates would stab another Cuban inmate who was sitting in the bleachers watching a softball game. They were archrivals, we heard. The Cuban in the bleachers had just moved out of the Receiving Orientation Unit (R&O) and was free to move around, while the other Cuban was just released from segregation and was also free to move around. The Cuban with the shank came up behind the bleachers, grabbing the other Cuban's left arm up and out of the way so he could stab his victim directly through his chest wall, into his heart. Greg's pager went off and he ran to the recreation yard not knowing what he would find. That was Greg's last day. The stabbing affected him to his core and he never returned to work.

Interesting how trauma affects nurses differently. The stabbing I know wouldn't have bothered me. Sure, my heart would have been racing due to the bleeding and doing CPR trying to keep the inmate's heart alive. And the fact that the inmate died before the ambulance arrived wouldn't have bothered me either. I had an emotional detachment to all this gore, probably embedded in me from working as a nursing assistant on an abdominal surgical unit. All the patients were in private rooms because of sepsis. The belly wounds on these patients were so deep and infected that each nurse needed four hands to irrigate and change the dressings. I was the other two hands. Nevertheless, in my mind, the visual of brains on the floor got to me.

By the end of my weekend days at Stillwater prison and before I transferred to Lino Lakes prison, if I could I would walk to the front of the prison and wait for the evening nurse who was relieving me, I would meet her in the rotunda, pass her the pager and any pertinent information, and wish her a good night. I would quickly continue walking through the security doors, the turn key, then out the front door.

On the top step outside the prison, I would stop and take a huge breath, knowing that unless there was a riot, I would not have to go back inside. And I was so grateful that once again, I had made it through another shift without a tier jumper. After eight years at Stillwater prison I transferred to Lino Lakes without witnessing one inmate either jumping or being shoved over a tier. Knowing there weren't any tiers at Lino, I was so relieved that my tier-anxiety would now dissipate. Other nurses weren't so lucky.

El Amin

The inmate I probably knew the least about but knew the longest was El Amin. I'm not even sure that was his real name; most Muslims' names were changed in prison. Even if they weren't Muslim, inmates changed their names because they found out it was free. So we had to put up with ridiculous names like X or Harley Davidson, or the best, Frito Bandito, before the Commissioner of Corrections put a stop to it. In those days the inmates didn't have to pay for a lawyer or court fees like regular citizens. Why? I don't know, but it bothered enough of us working in Corrections to complain to the Commissioner. He took a look into it, and that was the end of that.

El Amin probably got a freebie in the name-changing department and arrived in our Health Services ward in terrible shape. He not only had AIDS but his kidneys had shut down. Again, I don't know why he was incarcerated but with those two diagnoses it was probably IV drugs that had something to do with his lengthy sentence.

Three times a week a special-duty team took El Amin to a dialysis unit where he alone was dialyzed. Because of his HIV/AIDS diagnosis he was not allowed to be with patients with only renal failure. In the late eighties and nineties, before it was known how AIDS was transmitted, segregating patients with AIDS made sense; today it does not. Our job after El Amin returned from dialysis was to make sure his blood pressure remained stable and to give him his fistful of medications.

El Amin was a very quiet, peaceful person. Never bothered anyone in the ward, just prayed next to his bed on his prayer rug and kept to himself. I recall watching him hooking a new prayer rug. It was quite large with beautiful colors. I liked it so much I asked him if he would sell it to me. As staff, we were permitted to buy many things the inmates made. In the past I had bought handmade pine bunk beds for my boys, who used them until they went off to college. El Amin gave me a price of sixty dollars and we had a deal.

As the years rolled on, I transferred up to Lino Lakes prison, 31 miles northwest of Stillwater and El Amin was transferred there as well. We continued the same medical care for him post-dialysis. It was clear that he would never be a candidate for a kidney transplant and therefore would likely die from kidney disease rather than AIDS.

There were many AIDS patients in the prison and I became the appointed AIDS nurse. I worked specifically with the specialists who came to our secret Saturday clinic to treat them. We sent out covert passes to have those AIDS inmates come up to the health service building discreetly, so as not to draw any attention to them. All but one HIV/AIDS inmate lived in the general population and not in our ten-bed ward. Between the guards and the inmates, neither wanted anything to do with these men. There was lots of fear and ignorance about AIDS in those days, and, to make matters worse, it was stronger among the guards than the inmates.

Nevertheless, those inmates are probably alive today because of the care they received in prison and the follow-up care they received by those same doctors once they were released.

After ten years in Corrections, I had lost my sense of humor and I knew it was time to move on. I was lucky to land a position with the same infectious disease specialists and left Corrections for an HIV/AIDS research nurse position and at the same time enrolled at St. Mary's University to finish my bachelor's degree.

During my degree program I attended all-day Saturday classes. I heard from the HIV doctors that El Amin had been discharged to a nursing home close to my school in Minneapolis. He was quite debilitated, the doctors told me, so after class one day I went to visit him in the nursing home. Once I entered the front door, it was obvious this was a County facility—no one stopping you at the door, nursing assistants running around with medication cups trying to find the right resident, phones ringing off the hook. The patient's light board was lit up like a Christmas tree and the dozen or so residents in wheelchairs echoing each other, "Nurse, nurse, nurse." I saw El Amin's name with a room number on the board and went to find him.

Upon entering his room, I saw, in a bed close to the window, the small form of a body curled up under a light day-blanket you'd normally place over the knees of a patient in a wheelchair. There was a simple grocery bag, out of reach for him but close to his bed, filled with his life's belongings. Nothing personal was on his nightstand, just dust. El Amin was asleep, as was the other resident in the room. I leaned over and carefully pulled the cover down below his chin and he smiled. He was probably ninety pounds of skin and bones and too weak to get out of bed. I asked if I could help him unpack and he said sure. I placed a couple of books in his nightstand and plugged in a small radio next to his bed. I noticed a wheelchair and said, "How about I take you outside for some fresh air?" He agreed and I helped him into the chair and placed the blanket around his legs.

Out the front door we went and no one stopped us. As I walked him around the grounds, I asked him what food he missed the most and he replied, "McDonald's." I told him next time I came I would bring him a burger and fries. After I got him back into bed, he thanked me for coming, almost in a whisper. I could see he was dying. When I got back to work Monday I asked Dr. Sullivan if it would be okay to give El Amin a burger and fries from McDonald's and would that hurt his dialysis treatments? He replied, "Get him anything he wants."

So, for a few weeks, each Saturday I stopped after class with a cheeseburger and a large fries and took El Amin outside to eat them.

When he died, I guess there was only one relative to contact. He'd never had any visitors. I heard once that they all lived down South.

El Amin was one of the good guys who did a bad thing. There were many like him in prison, but there were also many bad guys who never learned from their bad deeds.

Manny

Manny avoided our health services like the plague. He was a heroin addict who, when he could get the stuff smuggled in, hibernated. No trips to sick call, no sign of him around. He would lose about forty pounds because he was too high to eat and a change in his appearance would alert our security staff that something was wrong.

The guards knew the 200 inmates in their cell hall and would report to us if they were suspicious of someone getting sick. Of course, being a concerned medical staff and always on the alert for a potential lawsuit, we tuned in to any weight loss.

Manny showed up by himself one Saturday and I happened to be the nurse on duty. He told the guard he needed to talk to me privately. We had a panic button in our exam room so I was not afraid or too concerned for my safety. What he told me was that he had been shooting heroin in his thigh and he had a bit of swelling around where he injected. After he dropped his pants, I saw an inflamed red-hot raging infection into his left thigh. Cellulitis would be the correct term, cured only by intravenous antibiotics and only by a trip to the hospital. He was upset that he had to leave the institution and go to the hospital because, "I'm a lifer and seeing the outside just makes my time worse. It's better if I just don't see anything but bars.

A special duty was set up and off he went to the hospital. I was surprised when he didn't come back before my shift was up. At the hospital the doctors said the infection was so bad that they had to take him to the operating room and open up his thigh. He was kept in the hospital a couple of days to run IV antibiotics and then returned to us for regular dressing changes.

Now, any nurse can change a dressing on a wound, but this was not an ordinary wound. Manny's thigh was thickly wrapped in gauze from his groin to his knee and as I unwrapped the bloody gauze, he informed me that we needed to "irrigate." That meant that the wound was deep. Manny was a large man, football player-type, and his wound was deep, about six inches into his thigh and cut open down to his knee. I had never seen a wound so large or so deep. It literally looked like a filleted thigh.

That was the beginning of my—shall I say intimate?—relationship with Manny. Each day over the noon hour he came to the health services for his dressing change and irrigations. As each day went by, slowly his wound granulated in and eventually healed. And while it was healing we talked. He told me why he was in prison. He said that he had been a drug addict during his growing up years and easily moved right into the life of crime because he was addicted and desperate. One day a drug deal went bad and he busted into an apartment where there were several people, including children. He had a gun and opened fire and killed them all, but he said, "I stopped at the kids." He could not understand why he stopped at the kids. He was high; he was out of his mind. When he couldn't get high in prison, he dealt with his crime, he had remorse and he knew he deserved to be there for life. But doing life didn't mean forever; at some point he would be released way before he died. He had no relationships outside of prison. He'd cut them all off, as he couldn't deal with the emotional pain.

He did everything in his power to never have to leave the prison for anything. He was a hard worker and even with the wound from hell, he never missed a day of work. Work kept him sane.

After Manny's wound healed, we again didn't see him around the prison halls or at the daily sick call. We assumed he was okay, yet on my rounds to the segregation unit one day, I noticed he was lying on a bunk. "Manny, that you? I wondered where you've been," I said.

He replied, "Oh nurse, I screwed up. You see, on New Year's Eve a few of the brothers got to celebrating and got a hold of some hooch, so after settling down at count time, I was lying there enjoying my high when the 'police' came by to tell me to turn my TV down. I attempted to roll forward to turn the dial, when actually I rolled right off my bunk and landed on my face, too high to catch myself. And that is why I'm here for thirty days."

"Doesn't look like you busted your nose," I said. "Take care, Manny, see ya around."

Minimum Security Unit

Minimum Security Unit (MSU) was the outside prison; to be eligible to live there, the inmate had to have one year left on his sentence. At six a.m. before going inside the main prison, we nurses would stop and hold a sick call for the MSU inmates. When it was my turn I would park my Toyota wagon in front of the building and usually, when returning, I would have a handful of inmates lying on the hood asking for a ride to work. Too tired, too cold—many reasons they couldn't walk a few blocks to the front door of the prison. I'd laugh and say, "You think I would lose my job over you guys?"

This MSU building housed approximately 100 inmates who all had jobs outside the prison walls, some in town, while many worked on the grounds, including maintaining a little graveyard across the street. Several worked in the employee cafeteria that was in the main prison building but outside the locked turnkey, the secure entrance to the prison. Our job was to stop at MSU and check in with the officer in charge who would hand us "kites" (blue sheets of paper with written messages to Health Services). We would triage the kites and quickly see any inmate needing medical attention.

One morning I had just missed an ambulance run where an inmate woke up and started projectile vomiting, hitting the wall next to his bunk. Thankfully he was on the lower bunk because this was not normal vomiting; he was vomiting blood from esophageal varices a terrible side effect chronic alcoholics can develop. Varices are enlarged veins like varicose veins seen in legs, but these veins burst in his esophagus. It was a medical emergency where he could have bled to death if the varices weren't quickly cauterized to stop the bleeding. The very competent night nurse started an IV, forcing fluids to stabilize the inmate until the ambulance arrived. She then helped the officers clean up the mess.

MSU was an interesting place because with only one year left on an inmate's sentence, you would think that he would be counting down the days to freedom, but some didn't, some walked away from the building with only a few months left to serve. A siren on the prison grounds would go off when there was a "walk away." This siren could be heard throughout the whole town of Stillwater, Minnesota. The inmate was always picked up, many times drunk, and returned to prison. But now, he didn't get the freedom of living outside the walls. Now he had to live in the segregation unit (seg), for a year. Seg; where for the first thirty days you aren't allowed any entertainment in your cell, meaning a TV or radio. Each day you are let out of your cell for one hour of exercise. You have a choice; you can be escorted outside to an enclosed basketball court and hope the nurse or anyone who walks by, will throw the basketball back when you over shoot. Or you can stay inside but outside your cell, and walk or run back and forth on the tier.

My youngest son, then in kindergarten, invited my parents to Grandparents Day, and after, I told them I'd take them to lunch at a surprise restaurant. Unbeknownst to them, we were headed to the Stillwater employee cafeteria. Here the MSU inmates cooked, served the meals and cleaned up the kitchen. After the Grandparents festivities and saying good-bye to my son, we left his grade school and headed to the prison. When I pulled into the parking lot, my mother almost fainted. In fact, she was terrified to enter the front door. My father, however, loved the idea.

My father had been a prisoner of war during WWII, held for three years in a Japanese prison camp, and he understood prisons. Lunch went well. The MSU inmates on the lunch line were thrilled to meet my parents and even gave my mother and me an extra couple of boiled eggs for our salads. After lunch I had planned a tour of the institution, starting with going through security. We entered the turnkey and my parents turned in their driver's licenses and put their visitor nametags on. The second barred gate slid open. We were now standing in the holding area, where the guard checked our purses before unlocking the last barred door. Upon entering the main hallway, we could see two large cell halls on the left and two large cell halls on the right, housing approximately 200 inmates in each.

At that point my mother was holding my arm tightly and my father started wandering around. During those years the prison had what they called "free movement," which meant that when the bell rang, all the cell hall doors opened and all the inmates were free to either go to a meal, out to work in the industry buildings or head to school. The bell rang and my mother clung to my arm like Velcro as hundreds of male inmates poured into the main hallway, hurriedly passing us, and yelling various greetings. It was like changing classes in high school only these were not students, they were incarcerated criminals. My mother, with a strained smile on her face, was begging me to turn around and get her out of there. My father had stopped at the chapel mid-hallway and was reading a plaque. When we caught up to him he said, "I would have liked to be in prison in a place like this. Nice they have a chapel."

There were guards at all the doors letting everyone in and out and within a matter of minutes the hallway settled down. It was not just my mother who was afraid to walk down that long, crowded hallway. Many times I would be sent to the front door of the prison to escort one of our doctors to the Health Services building. One doctor whom I often escorted both in and out of the building asked me once if I was ever scared. I said, "Not really. I feel safer here than in downtown Minneapolis." At least the majority of the inmates weren't drugged up and respected the hospital staff, as they knew we were there to help them. However, I was always acutely aware of my surroundings and never let my guard down.

Wait… there were a couple of naive moves I made when I was first hired. One was that I was juggling a cart full of medications to be passed out at the pill window, aka the laundry, during the inmates' dinner hour. I had just gotten the keys to open the laundry door from the guard sitting behind glass, across the hall in the security center, but I couldn't get the door to unlock. A diagnosed bipolar inmate, whom we watched swallow his daily psych medications, was walking by while I was struggling and offered to help me unlock the door, so I gave him the keys. Immediately I knew that was a wrong move but the inmate just unlocked the door and gave me back the keys like an ordinary person would. I thanked him and he left the area. The guard across the hall watched the whole incident and was shaking his head. He did not make a big deal out of it but warned me not to do that again.

My second naive move was during my first lockdown. I was in a cell hall passing out insulin to several diabetics who mostly lived on the flag. To efficiently make use of my time, I found all the guys on the flag and passed out all the boxes that held their insulin, an alcohol wipe and a syringe. When I went back to collect them, an officer was waiting for me. He was quick to let me know that I should wait after each inmate injected himself before going to the next cell. He explained that the Tupperware box holding the syringe could be passed down from cell to cell in a heartbeat and upon its return, the syringe would be missing, never to be found. A syringe in prison was like scoring a brick of cocaine on the streets. Lesson learned!

As far as my parents ever returning to the prison cafe, no, that never happened, but it was one of my father's favorite stories to tell the grandkids: the day he and Grandma went to prison.

*(The "turnkey" was the main security checkpoint while entering the prison; the metal-barred doors would slide open and you would step inside a waiting area with more bars in front of you. On your left was a closed, glassed booth where once the sliding barred door closed behind you the officer in the booth would process you through security. As a visitor you would drop your driver's license into the sliding drawer the officer operated before he would issue you a visitor's nametag. If you were law enforcement you had to turn in your gun. All returned when you exited the turnkey).

Medical Transport

Riding along accompanying felons to medical appointments was not an everyday assignment. However, there were those inmates who our officers just didn't want to deal with based on their medical or mental condition. This is when we, being the prison nurses, would be asked to accompany them to a clinic appointment outside the prison.

I volunteered, not really knowing what I was getting myself into. I figured a change in duties would be interesting, at least for one day.

The prison transport van was out in front of the prison along with another prison vehicle called the "chase car" right behind it. The officers were inside the prison in the holding cell shackling the inmates, five of them with wrist cuffs attached to chains, then attached to ankle cuffs, so it was slow moving up and down the front steps, let alone into the van.

Once all the medical records were gathered and the inmates settled into their seats, the officers turned to me and said, "Oh, plenty of room for you in the back." In between a couple of felons I was placed. The inmate I was accompanying had been fighting the Japanese in his head for some time. He was scheduled for a sigmoidoscopy for suspected cancer. He was on my left side by the window and probably a rapist was on my right side. The door closed and I realized the van was fashioned after police cars where the doors are locked on the inside, with no way out.

I admit I am claustrophobic and as soon as the doors closed, I thought, *this isn't going to work*. I had three inmates sitting behind me, two on either side of me all shackled, yes, but I'm sure if they wanted to, they could figure out a way to harm me. Obviously the officers didn't think I was at risk.

The two officers proceeded to blast some rock station loudly through the back speakers where I was suffering and plotting ways to kill them. The blasting music, plus the wire mesh with plexiglass dividing us, kept any conversation with the guards inaudible. Thank the good Lord the ride to this hospital was less than half an hour and I could get out in one piece. What were those guys thinking? I could have been held hostage in a locked prison van…right? What would be an inmate's plan who was already shackled, already doing time and more interested in seeing the outside flying by than harming this prison nurse they've seen daily for the past eight years? I was glaring at those two idiots when I saw them giggling in the rearview mirror.

Once the van stopped and the armored car doors opened, I let them know that they weren't funny, and I reminded them that I would be sitting in the front seat on the way back and we would be listening to my station, no discussion.

The inmates were herded into a private entrance in the back of the hospital where they were placed in a holding cell with benches attached to the walls. Here they would sit literally all day, until every last one of them was seen in the various specialty clinics. Most of these runs to the hospital were daily, as there were too many medical conditions that needed a second opinion or an expert evaluation that couldn't be done by our prison physicians because of lack of expertise or diagnostic equipment.

The inmates were a litigious group, so covering all medical bases was important in deterring lawsuits.

With the inmates securely behind locked doors, I was free to visit with the correctional nurse whose job was to smoothly run the prisoners' clinic appointments and to be vigilant along with the officers that there would not be any interaction with any other person while the inmate was outside the prison facility.

It had happened in the past that an inmate would find out when he had a medical appointment outside the prison and he would notify a friend or relative to meet him and sometimes an escape was planned. Most of these trysts were squelched well before they got off the ground because there were security personnel listening in on the inmate's phone conversations. Sometimes a medical person unaware of the security breach would tell the inmate when his next appointment would be and, if found out by prison staff, the appointment was immediately cancelled.

It was time to accompany inmate Nelson to his sigmoidoscopy. We pushed him in a wheelchair up to the GI clinic and we were let into another back entrance; here we were placed in an exam room with machines. Nelson was a cranky older man with Alzheimer's and we suspected some type of cancer was brewing somewhere in him as he was losing an abnormal amount of weight.

The nurse instructed us to help him undress and I calmly spoke to him about what we were going to do and he was acting like he understood. We had him undressed and covered by a blanket when the doctor arrived.

For the procedure the doctor had Nelson kneel on the table with his butt up in the air. This started a tirade of swearing and seething directed at the Japanese while the doctor placed the scope in his rectum for the exam. Nelson did cooperate but didn't like it and continued to fight his imaginary enemies throughout the procedure.

To me the exam went quickly and efficiently and we were able to calm Nelson down enough to get him dressed and back in the wheelchair. Unfortunately for the inmate, the doctor had seen a tumor, biopsied it and figured Nelson already had an advanced cancer.

Back in the holding tank, we left Nelson with the rest of the inmates and the officers ran back and forth to different clinics for the medical records and new doctor's orders until three p.m. when we were all finished. Shackling the inmates together by chains again, we started the slow-moving train back to the van.

This time I was not fooled by the seating arrangement and I promptly planted myself in the front seat. Controlling the radio now, I quickly tuned in 99.5 FM, the classical music station, where Mozart and his friends, Bach and Haydn, worked their magic with their captive audience, all the way back to prison.

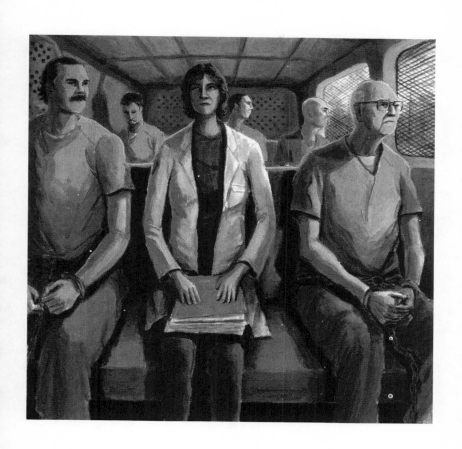

Tier 3:

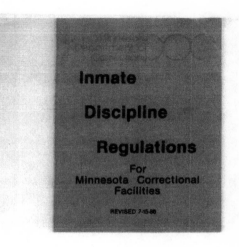

RULE   VIOLATIONS

PENALTIES FOR DISCIPLINARY
INFRACTIONS

Abbreviations are:

Loss of Privileges	LOP	
Restrictive Segregation	RS	
Segregation	SEG	
Potential Good Time Loss	PGTL	

Days LOP	Days RS	Days SEG	Days PGTL up to

Cover of the "Inmate Discipline Regulations," (1986)

40. Escape or Attempted Escape

No inmate shall without lawful authority depart from the institution, the institution grounds, or the custody of a supervising person; or aid another by providing him/her with the necessary materials or means to facilitate an escape.

Days (Lop)	Days (RS)	Days (SEG)	Days (PGTL up to)
		Infraction Penalty	
		90-360	180

Escape

During my ten years behind bars there were many mini attempts at escaping. Some really lame attempts, like the guy in our hospital ward who was, nightly, using some sort of makeshift file to saw the bars on the bathroom window. If he got through them, it would place him in an outside recreation area surrounded by a fence he'd have to scale and would still be inside the prison compound. Next he'd have to scale the wall before going over it where the tower guards with their rifles would be standing at the top, ready to shoot him down.

There was one Cuban inmate who, in broad daylight, scrambled up the wall like a jackrabbit and did manage to throw himself over it without being shot—only to be caught ten minutes later while running in an adjacent open field. The officer hearing on the radio that this inmate was over the wall was close to the front door of the prison; he immediately jumped on his motorcycle parked across the street. He charged through the field and almost ran the inmate over, or at least the inmate thought he would. Into segregation this inmate went for a year, the charge for an escape.

However, there were a couple of serious attempts, which remain very clear to me because they were medical visits and our nurses were involved. Clinic visits outside the prison walls were a big deal. We had a contracted, secure medical facility with security beds thirty miles from the prison, where all our specialty appointments took place, usually daily. The rule was that the inmates never knew when they would be going to the hospital. If a surgery were planned for the next day, the evening nurse would stop by the inmate's cell after everyone was locked in for the night and the phones were turned off. The nurse would only tell the inmate not to eat or drink after midnight. About five a.m., a guard would come by and take the inmate to the security center to wait for all the other inmates also scheduled to go to the hospital, while another guard was getting the cuffs and chains set up.

Once at the hospital, the inmates were corralled like cattle into another security unit to wait for their appointments. This was the daily norm for specialty medical appointments, with a few exceptions. Sometimes an inmate had to see a private physician outside the secure medical facility; for example, Jones, who was blind. His doctor's office was in downtown Minneapolis. I don't recall the history of the relationship between this doctor and Jones, only that it probably was related to Jones's glass left eye. That morning, per rote, all security systems were in place, the inmate was picked up by the guards and securely cuffed, and the van was ready to head out for an appointment with the eye doctor by six a.m. This doctor scheduled Jones early, to be in and out before clinic opened for regular patients.

We heard at first that everything was going well, the doctor and nurse were attending to inmate Jones's fake eye, when suddenly an ex-inmate, Max, an old friend of Jones's, stormed the office armed with a gun and stole the prison van with Jones in it. The doctor, his nurse, and the two guards were not hurt but were scared to death. With Max at the wheel, Jones raced to his ex-girl friend's apartment and proceeded to rape her while her young child was outside the bedroom. At the same time the police were in hot pursuit and broke down the door to the apartment and shot inmate Jones to death, while Max went unwillingly back to prison. Apart from the rape, the girlfriend and child were unharmed.

This left us all asking, "Where was the breach in security?" It had to be within this doctor's office, where probably a naïve employee while answering the phone would freely give out the day and time of a patient's next appointment. Max would have called, because if Jones called from the prison, the call would automatically state that it is from a correctional facility. Needless to say, everyone suffered in this terrible event. The two officers took mental health leaves and one never returned to work; I spotted him later working as a TSA agent at the Minneapolis airport. I can only imagine the trauma the girlfriend and her child lived through.

The second serious escape attempt happened one evening when I was not working. Another nurse, Mike, was on duty and the officer in charge of the prison that night was Lt. Howard McClish. The evening was uneventful until there was some sort of altercation where an inmate stated he had been attacked and stabbed and needed to be rushed to the hospital. He carried on and on and was rushed to the front of the prison on a gurney, writhing in pain. The compassionate nurse, Mike, was trying to check the inmate out and assess the injuries but was met with such resistance because of this inmate's pain, specifically in the groin area, that he gave up and told the officers to cuff him to the gurney and call the ambulance.

The ambulance arrived and two guards got in the back with the inmate while one guard followed in the "chase car." Inside the ambulance, the inmate continued to carry on and begged the officers to un-cuff just one wrist so that he could get more comfortable. And they did. Hey, what could happen? He was cuffed at three other

71

points on the gurney while racing down the freeway with sirens and lights flashing. But the unthinkable did happen.

Slowly this inmate pulled a small gun from his groin area. The ambulance driver tuned into what was happening behind him and kept driving but at the same time was calling the prison, letting Lt. McClish know what was up. Lt. McClish was in contact with the "chase car" by radio and after assessing the information and evaluating whether this inmate actually had a real gun, he told the guard to "take the ambulance"—meaning, make the ambulance pull over. A few arguments took place between the guards and their commander, but in the end, the "chase car" made the ambulance pull over by trying to run it off the road, and the officer opened the ambulance door and took the gun from the inmate. Under examination, it was revealed that the so-called gun was perfectly made in the industry's wood shop and expertly painted to look like a real gun.

Later we learned that Lt. McClish's wisdom in making this call was from his years working in this prison. He knew that if there was a gun inside those walls, one of the snitches would have ratted that inmate out and McClish knew all the snitches.

The next morning I was doing my rounds in the segregation unit and, standing at the bars of his cell was the supposedly stabbed victim calling me over. He said, "Nurse, please tell Mike I hope he doesn't get into any trouble. This was all my fault. Tell him I'm very sorry."

Another year in segregation for this guy; hardly worth stabbing yourself for a night out in an ambulance and a year in the "hole."

Mark Adams*

B ase files were available to be read by staff if they so desired; I did
not, ever. It was my mantra that these convicts had been judged and
sentenced and it wasn't up to me to make them any more miserable
than they already were. Each day I mentally adjusted my thinking
that each interaction with a rapist or murderer was a new day, I didn't
need to know the crime, I needed to know what was happening with
that inmate on that day, that moment, and go from there. In nursing
and healthcare when dealing with difficult patients in order to avoid
burnout you have to take your personal judgment and the client' past
history out of the interaction and focus only on the present. Past,
repeat behaviors were just that, in the past. And that attitude worked
until I met Mark Adams.

On March 25, 1987, Mark brutally and savagely murdered the
brother of a close friend of mine. Bob, my friend Kathy's brother,
was engaged to a woman who Mark had had a prior relationship
with; however, she had ended it and was now engaged to Bob. Mark
threatened that they would not make it to the altar. He slashed their
car tires and continued to threaten them to the point where the couple would call many times a day and check in with each other, this
was pre cell phones. One morning, close to the wedding date, Mark
broke into Bob and his fiancé's apartment and when Bob arrived
home, Mark opened fire execution style, hitting Bob's head and

chest seven times. He next took the rifle butt and smashed the side of Bob's face so hard it left an imprint on the side of his head. He died instantly.

On June 20, 1987, Mark got the maximum sentence, life with the possibility of parole. However, a life sentence in Minnesota at that time was only seventeen and a half years; the sentencing guidelines changed shortly thereafter to thirty years.

Mark arrived at Stillwater Prison one evening while I was the only nurse on duty. I was called to do his intake, not knowing whom I was interviewing. I met him in the front conference room and prepared to ask him all my medical questions. I froze when he gave me his name.

Sitting across from me was a short, nondescript, boyish-looking, white kid. I noticed how agreeable he was to whatever the officer was asking him to do, actually, overly agreeable. He was very forthcoming with all his answers to my medical questions. I knew right away what type of inmate he was going to be, a suck-up. And from that day forward he never caused any problems while doing his time. He played the good-boy act and wound up being known as an inmate we as staff, could call upon when needing extra help on a project. To be called out of his day job to go to another area inside the prison and be trusted to do another job on top of his work was a real coup for an inmate. This went on for seventeen years.

After fourteen years of incarceration, Mark petitioned for an early release. Bob's family, his fiancée and her children wrote letters to the Commissioner of Corrections and the parole board. On the day of the hearing they also did a presentation. At this review Mark was denied release for six years. On schedule, six years later another hearing took place and again the family wrote letters and did a presentation voicing their concerns. Mark was given another six years before he would be reviewed again.

The families were pleased they prevented Mark's release for twenty-six years. When the next hearing was scheduled six years later, the family stood firm and repeated the letters and presentation. Only this time he was given just two years before his next review. Worried now, the family was certain in two years Mark would get out of prison, until it was discovered that Mark had written a letter to one of the children of his ex- fiancée. The orders had been clear: **No Contact** for the rest of his life with any of the families. At the two-year review, Mark's infraction gave him another year in prison.

Finally, in January 2017, after close to thirty years of incarceration, Mark entered a Work Release program. All was going well until just six days before his release date of September 12, 2017. Mark again violated his release by having some type of weapon and was returned to prison, where he resides today.

For a man who was so desperate to be released at fourteen years of a then-seventeen-year life sentence, Mark seems to have been worn down through his thirty-plus years of incarceration. What fool would jeopardize his release by knowingly possessing a weapon he knew would potentially cancel his release?

I had seen it before. Old convicts, dependent on inhalers and heart medications, done serving their time, saying goodbye to their cronies, while carrying two weeks worth of medications and fifty dollars "key money," heading to the bus stop, only to sucker-punch the guard opening the front door for him. "Sorry, man, back in you go!"

So relieved to be back in the cellblock, and back to his dysfunctional family where he will happily die on his bunk, rather than face the reality of the outside world he left a lifetime ago.

* All names have been changed.

Porn

It was within the first few years that I worked there, Stillwater State Prison, where I was getting more and more annoyed by what was showing on the inmates' TVs and cell walls. Particularly in the Receiving and Orientation Unit where there was only one TV but at least fifty inmates glued to it. Sometimes the movie was *Cheerleaders Gone Wild,* which as I recall was played over and over again. An inmate sat in the video room and inserted the VCR tape and the movies came through a closed circuit TV. Supposedly the videos went through a selection process by a committee that monitored their appropriateness, supposedly the same movies seen in family theaters. Yeah, right.

I would appear in the cell hall wearing my white lab coat, bringing insulin or some medication to a newbie. The guard would barely look up as I found my way up the steps to the wooden throne-like platform, where he was seated at a desk. The guard would yell the inmate's name to come and meet me on the flag. Everyone was so engrossed in watching the flesh of some porn star bouncing around in front of them that they didn't even look up. "Yuck" was my reaction.

When I made my rounds in cell halls where the inmates were locked in because it was "count time" or the whole prison was locked down, I would have to walk the tiers to find the person I needed to speak to. Many times when I found the cell, the inmate was cordial as I told him some personal medical news, like he should not eat or drink after midnight. Never did we say that the inmate's surgery or special test would be performed the next day; that would have been a security breach. But what was not cordial was my view of how he had decorated his cell walls.

Wallpapered on the ceiling and all three walls were magazine centerfolds of naked women, predominantly featuring women's crotches. It was pretty hard to focus on the seriousness of my medical business when surrounded by this décor; the prison environment was hard enough without this distasteful distraction.

As employees we had a suggestion box called "Brite Ideas," where we could write a suggestion that would be sent to the Warden. One night I was so grossed out after making my rounds in the cell halls that I decided to submit a "Brite Idea."

I didn't hear anything and didn't think I would until one particular Saturday morning. I was working by myself and received a call from the Attorney General's Office stating that the Warden had received my "Brite Idea" and because of me, as well as a social worker at Oak Park Prison with the same concerns, the Commissioner of Corrections ordered a Statewide Task Force to resolve this issue. Later my "Brite Idea" was in my mailbox with a note from the Warden that said, "*As you know, a committee has been formed (you're on it) to come up with a solution to the problem. Good idea. Thanks. Robert Erickson.*"

Now, I'm not saying that every inmate, all 1400 of them, decorated their cells in the same pornographic manner, but it was a huge percentage, which made me very uncomfortable while trying to do my job.

The porn task force started and, fortunately, we had a lawyer from the Attorney General's Office who consistently brought the team back into focus. Yes, this was the inmates' home, but equally important, it was a workplace to thousands of employees. Funny how the males on the task force just couldn't quite grasp that concept. We met for months, and ideas of what and how much the inmates could display on their walls were batted around. We had debates like define "skimpy" when speaking about a woman in a bathing suit, and was that appropriate to hang on an inmate's wall? Pictures of violence against women, these guys got that, but different degrees of clothing, or lack of it, on women seemed okay to them. And what if we decided that the inmates could only hang their wife's picture in an 8x10 frame; was that okay even if she was naked?

In the end we came to an agreement: that inmates could have naked pictures of women, as long as they were placed in a scrapbook and were not displayed while employees were in and around their cells. They could keep their scrapbooks in their footlockers or under their mattresses, out of sight. Nothing could be hung on the cell walls—fire hazard!

Interestingly enough, the fight was just beginning with this new inmate rule, and it wasn't from the inmates. Many officers in our prison didn't understand the simple principle that this was their workplace, not the inmate's home. Yes, the crooks stayed overnight and ate there, but it still was our workplace, not their home. So to enforce this new policy, the guards had to tell the inmates to take the porn off the walls and if told the inmates acted immediately, the guards just didn't enforce the rule. Every single day when I came upon cell walls covered in porn, I discreetly wrote the cell number down and upon leaving the area gave my list to whoever was in charge. This always induced lively banter like, "Hey, Nurse Anita (Hill), don't you wear a bathing suit when you go swimming?" Moronic statements out of these dunderheads I didn't need. None of them knew I had been an instigator in this new rule and because it wasn't my place to tell an inmate what the cell hall rules were, the guards had to enforce the rule and the inmates absolutely did what they were told. Many, not all, of the guards were just too lazy to walk up to the tier and let the inmate know the pictures had to come down. Many, not all, were RODs (retired on duty) and just too busy counting down their days 'till retirement. But the rest of the nurses and I were hyper-vigilant and relentless when it came to enforcing this new rule. If the smut was still on the walls the next time we came through, we reported it up the chain of command. It took almost two years after the new porn law was in place before the guards took it seriously.

The best time for a good cell-housecleaning was during a lockdown. Usually a couple times a year the whole prison would "lock down," where no inmates were allowed to leave their cells; therefore, everything had to be delivered to them.

Lockdowns were a ton of work for all of us. We delivered hundreds of medications and insulin during the day and evening shifts, as well as answering all the inmates' requests, written via "kites." Kites were written messages to Health Services; they were picked up from the cell halls and delivered to us all day. Most kites were requesting a nurse to come to an inmate's cell because he was sick, and during a summer lockdown, this meant a very hot, sweaty trek to the cell.

Teams of staff members went cell to cell until the whole prison was checked for contraband; this could take up to two weeks. While an inmate's cell was being "shaken down," the inmate was cuffed to the bars outside his cell. The guards would basically tear everything off the walls, dump out the inmate's footlocker and all containers, and make a big mess for the inmate to clean up once they were through. The guards would write the inmate up if they found any contraband.

During one lockdown, the guards returned to us a bag full of Tylenol, two tabs wrapped in each packet. There must have been a thousand of them. This inmate would stop at the "pill window" located in the laundry, open during supper, where the pharmacy nurse would daily hand out over-the-counter medications as well as prescription medications. Obviously the inmate was not taking the Tylenol. Probably this daily routine was just to make eye contact or, if he was lucky, touch the nurse's hand. Inmates do some strange things but this routine was pretty benign and I doubt he was written up for it.

During a lockdown was the best time to get the smut out of the cells and yet several officers still did not enforce the new porn rule, which had been in effect for two years. Many guards had their own interpretation of the rule. I heard these two: "Any picture could be hung in a cell as long as it was in an 8x10 "frame" and "Inmates can only hang pictures on the left wall." I confronted the officers about where they heard "the left wall" and asked, "Was that why the cell you had just cleaned had porn floor to ceiling but only on the "left wall"? Their response was, "They told us." Finally their superior showed up and read them the official Policy on Offensive Material 3.226.0. End of discussion.

Later that day the Warden and I were leaving the building at the same time. We chatted about the new porn policy and I told him about today's events during an inmate shakedown and how I thought I caused a ruckus in the cell hall. He replied, "No, you didn't. As they say in the army, ten percent of the group doesn't hear."

I eventually left Corrections, but the prison porn battles went on for almost ten more years. Now it had moved exclusively into the mailroom. A new female Commissioner expanded the original policy where letters and magazines with nudity in them would be banned. There were some exceptions, *Playboy* and *Sports Illustrated Swimsuit Issue*. All letters containing pictures or copies of pictures depicting nudity would be destroyed. This policy was specific for the prison officers who worked in the mailroom checking for contraband: they had the same workplace rights as those in the cell halls, to be able to work in a safe, non-offensive environment. And boy, did the Commissioner hear it. The media had a field day. Headlines in the *Minneapolis Tribune, City Pages* and the *St. Paul Pioneer Press* included: "Playboy in Prisons," "Smut-free sentencing," "Nude magazines banned in Minnesota prisons," "MCLU director says material is constitutionally protected," "Look, Sheryl: No Pictures: a recommended reading list for people that live in big houses."

This barrage of articles and letters to the editor against the Commissioner didn't sit well with me, so in a letter I reached out to her and gave her the detailed facts of the history of prison porn and I thanked her for supporting the policy. At the same time I wrote a letter to the editors of the local newspapers titled:

Missing the (Prison-porn) Point

Corrections Commissioner Sheryl Ramstad Hvass is under fire with her new policy banning magazines such as Playboy *and* Penthouse, *in the state correctional institutions. Lately, there have been numerous articles in the* St. Paul Pioneer Press *and the* Minneapolis Tribune *addressing this topic. None of the articles or letters to the editor has captured the bottom line of this issue.... Lawsuits.*

Minnesota employs approximately 3000 men and women in our correctional system. This is their job, some for their entire career and some like myself, who worked in the system for ten years. Like any other job, this is where the employee spends eight hours a day, forty hours a week. Like any other job, the employee has the right to work in a non-offensive, harassment-free environment. Same rules apply in prison.

Unfortunately, because the inmates' cells are viewed as their homes, the thinking becomes blurred. Most inmates and some staff think it's ok to have these types of magazines. Some officers have said, "It makes my job easier."

In 1989 a policy was written to clean up the smut inside the prison walls. Off came the naked women in lewd positions that were wallpapered to the inmate's cell. You could finally stand in front of a cell [and] talk to an inmate without being grossed out by what he viewed as great decorating. At the same time the videos were reviewed. (I used to think if I could just walk past the common television without seeing any gangbanging, it was a good shift.) Out went the XXX videos on the prison closed-circuit channel.

Now we are down to magazines. Yes, Playboy *magazine seems pretty lame to be banning, but have you forgotten about the employee who sorts the mail and checks for contraband? He or she has the same workplace rights as you do. Free of harassment, in a safe non-offensive environment.*

This policy has little to do with the inmates and their particular crime[s]; this policy has everything to do with the rights of an employee and the obligations of the employer. That employer is Sheryl Ramstad Hvass, the Commissioner of Corrections.

Now I ask you, in your workplace, how many times a day do you view scantily clad women or men?

I received a very thoughtful thank you note from the Commissioner stating… "It is unfortunate that your earlier efforts to heighten people's sensitivity went largely unnoticed. Your reinforcement of the policy we announced is gratifying. Thank you for sharing your views with me, Ellen, as well as for your courage to voice those views at a time when there was not a receptive audience or management, but because it was the right thing to do."

Sincerely,
Sheryl Ramstad Hvass
February 10, 2001

Bonsai

Next to the Health Services building was a greenhouse, where inside there was a sponsored Bonsai program. The inmates' newspaper, called *The Prison Mirror*, reported it was called the MCF-Stillwater Bonsai Club and was sponsored by the Minnesota Bonsai Society. The Japanese term Bonsai literally means "planted in a container," but the art form of creating a bonsai tree stems from an ancient Chinese practice, which evolved under the influence of Japanese Zen Buddhism. The bonsai tree basically represents peace, balance, and harmony and all that is good in the world. There were eleven members who nurtured one hundred or so miniature trees, shrubs, and other plants in this club, which also had a board of directors, president, vice president, secretary and treasurer. The club's goal was to become self-sufficient by selling their quality trees outside the prison walls. One member said, in a *Prison Mirror* article, that working on his trees was like an escape from regular prison life. And the consensus among the active members was that this provided an excellent opportunity for the individual to work toward self-rehabilitation, to learn respect, concern, communication, and relationship development.

Until one day, there was an attempted murder in the greenhouse.

Count time in the prison was taken very seriously. One beautiful spring day at 11:30 a.m. when all inmates were ordered to return to their cells to be counted, it was strange that we didn't hear the usual "Count clear" from the officers' radios. And it was even stranger when by 12:00 noon, count still was not cleared. Sometimes we were amazed how quickly the whole prison of 1400 inmates could be accounted for in less than fifteen minutes. All cell halls were walked tier by tier by the guards, who made sure there was a body within each cell. Then at the end of each tier, they shouted their count down to the officer at the desk. All departments holding inmates for work—e.g., kitchen staff—called in their numbers of inmates to the security center, which relayed names and numbers to the count desk. Efficiently done at 11:30 a.m., "count time" was usually short and uneventful; everyone was hungry for lunch.

We in Health Services were watching out the front windows nervously waiting for something to happen when suddenly we could see, bursting out the side door of the main building, the "squad" (the police force within the prison) racing to the horticulture greenhouse next door to us. Over the radios we heard "Code 3 medical," and we took off. Found under one of the potting tables was the nearly lifeless body of a very small, white inmate. He was breathing but he had sustained severe head wounds, which we could see were delivered by a bloody shovel lying next to him. We stabilized the inmate and an ambulance was called to transport him to the security hospital.

Because none of the inmates were talking, no one was charged with the assault, therefore upon discharge from the hospital, this inmate was moved to the Protective Custody Unit (PCU). This was a unit that housed approximately 50-100 inmates whose lives had been threatened or whose cases were all over the media, or who were known pedophiles, and all these inmates needed extra protection from the inmates in the general population.

Later that week while making rounds with the prison physician, we stopped in PCU to check on the inmate who had been assaulted. His head wounds were healing nicely but he had no recall of what happened to him. He knew he had been attacked or had an accident, but it wasn't clear to him, which it was. He didn't know why he was in prison either, and with this confusion, the officers placed him on the flag to keep an eye on him.

Outside PCU the word from the guards was that this inmate was a pedophile. Never reading a base file, I had no interest in looking it up. However, one inmate described him to me stating, "He was always running his mouth," he "never shut up," and he was "constantly boasting about his victims." The inmates in the greenhouse apparently had had enough of him. Now, amongst the inmates who knew him, he was renamed "shovelhead."

One day while Bill, a Bonsai participant and one of our diabetics, and I were walking between buildings, I asked him what the update was to the "shovelhead" incident; had anyone been charged? He responded, "The guy had a big mouth and there's a code in prison...silence."

I never asked again. I had just learned an unconventional prison policy: the inmates take care of their own. No one was ever charged for the attempted murder and the Bonsai program continued to flourish through the 1990s.

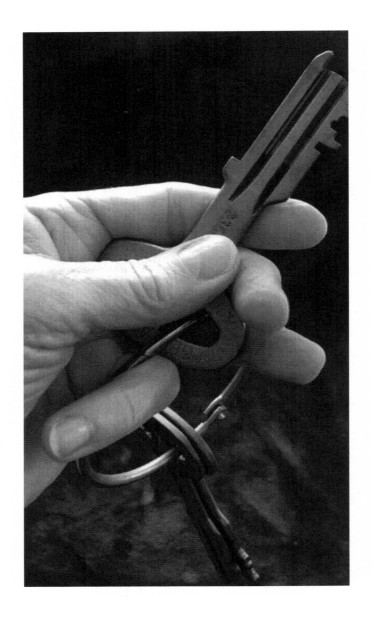

Stillwater prison cell hall keys

Fallen Prey:
Guards, Teachers and Nurses

Workplace romances can be common but are usually frowned upon; chances are they might become complicated and sometimes don't end well. Take that same workplace romance inside a prison where an inmate and a staff member become involved and magnify the word *complicated* ten-fold.

I never understood why some employees became romantically involved with the cons. The guy is obviously locked up, unable to take you on dates. There would be no flowers, no sex, just long hand-written letters expressing his endless love for you. When he can get time on the phone, he'll call you and after the operator asks if you want to accept a collect call from an inmate in a correctional facility, you'll accept and there he'll be, ready to blather his intense love for you. If you're busy and don't pick up right away, get ready for some verbal abuse. In his mind, you don't keep your man waiting. Next, your guy can't keep a secret and will shoot his mouth off about you to the other inmates and before you know it someone will snitch him out. Usually the snitch is another inmate who has issues with you and this is his covert payback. The administration is involved now, and you are fired. So was he worth it?

After my six months on the night shift I was hired to work 3rd watch (3-11 p.m. shift), because the nurse I was replacing was fired after her affair with a lifer was found out. All this took place in the Health Service building where the lifer was the swamper (janitor allowed to live in the ward), and the nurse worked the shift alone. With only one guard posted in the building, I guess it was easy for the two of them to get together. This lifer was an okay inmate, as many were. He had a 1960s look, slick-backed hair like Elvis. He never caused any trouble and was always respectful to the staff.

The other nurses told me that this nurse, sadly, was a mother of six kids, with a great husband. The inmate had committed a horrendous murder, never to see the light of day. She lost everything, her job and her family, only to hide her identity by donning a wig trying to get into the visitation room at Oak Park prison, Minnesota's only level five maximum-security prison, where the inmate was transferred. She was beautiful, the guards said, and many of our single officers were disappointed when she chose the inmate over them. Had they known, they lamented, they would have "helped her out." Years later the inmate was transferred to Lino Lakes prison where the nurse was still visiting him, without the wig.

Another seasoned officer-turned-case manager took up with a repeat felon she had been working with. Case managers could meet privately in an office within the cellblock. What made this relationship even more complex was that she was married to another officer working the same shift. It was painful for us to watch her husband have to live through her craziness. She didn't lose her job but was caught again, trying to visit the inmate when he was transferred to Lino Lakes prison. We supported her husband and, with therapy, she stopped the inmate relationship and was working on her marriage.

Minnesota's prisons didn't just encourage inmates to go to school while incarcerated, it was mandatory. All inmates without a GED had to attend school until they obtained their high school equivalency diploma. And luckily for them, one of the teachers was a beautiful woman. She was married to a doctor, didn't have children, and she left her husband for an inmate in her class. Eventually the inmate was released and her sister told me they became a couple.

Later, as I tried to understand the dynamics of these relationships, I realized that the inmates had all day, every day, to try to seduce women who came to the prison on a regular basis, whether for security work or teaching. The prisoners were continuously studying them to find out how to tap into their weaknesses. They were always after their innermost secrets while showering them with compliments. Known by their diagnoses of sociopath or personality disorder, these men were sly, persistent and patient. They had the time to weave their webs and trap their prey, however long it took. These women didn't stop the inmates' pursuit by using my usual sassy line: "Ha, you've been locked up too long." Instead, they relished the courtship.

Those female employees were not new to Corrections either. They had worked in the system for years and had become complacent toward their environment, letting their guard down by blurring the lines of reality from inside vs outside the walls. Forgetting their orientation training where the captain states with a grin, "The inmates didn't get to prison for singing off-key in a boys' choir." We were taught that you don't go to prison for minor offenses you go to jail. You go to prison because those minor offenses were repeated over and over until an event, sometimes a horrific event, changed the inmate's life forever. These were simple criminology facts, ignored or forgotten by these women so blinded by love.

It made more sense to me when a correctional officer fell to an inmate. The guards in the cell halls had face-to-face interactions with 200 inmates multiple times a day—locking and unlocking the cell block door, the inmate's cell, or pat-down searches after an inmate returned from work or meals. Calling an inmate down from the tier for a message, or a pass for an appointment, passing out mail or a meal supplement for a sick inmate, led to numerous interactions with the officers. Count-time, four times a day, was where the guards walked the tiers, cell by cell, and counted breathing bodies to make sure the number of bodies matched the total prison-count. During all these exchanges the inmates and guards may engage in friendly banter, leading some officers to think that "Hey, they're not all bad."

Occasionally inmates and guards came from the same neighborhoods. This information was supposed to be reported to the administration if the guard felt there would be a problem. It would be easy to see how the familiarity of coming from the same "hood" could make an inmate feel like he had some sort of bond with the guard. Unknowingly, some officers were lured into an inmate's underworld, first by ignoring an inmate's minor offense like overlooking an inmate from his "hood" bringing more food back from dinner than what was allowed. Maybe it was a couple pieces of fruit that later would be fermented into "hooch." Eventually the same inmate breaks another rule, like being a couple minutes late checking into the cellblock, but it's not a big deal because the bell just rang so the guard lets this inmate slide by again. That is, until the guard looks the other way at all these minor offenses because the guard and this inmate are kind of "brothers" and this inmate respects the guard, or so he says. Months go by and this same inmate tells this guard he can make some extra money by bringing drugs into the prison; after all, they're friends. This inmate has compiled a whole list of infractions this officer has not enforced and threatens to report him to the Warden.

Or worse yet, a guard will become lax with his personal information because it's normal to talk about your kids on Father's Day and what a bummer you have to work every Sunday. You're kicked back in your cell block chair, boots up on the desk, just "shootin' the shit" with a couple of the cons you've known for years, just waiting for your relief to show up. That same inmate, the one who says he respects you, now overhears the names of your kids and uses them as collateral to get you to do what he wants. He lets you know that he has friends on the street and though you're divorced, he knows where your ex-wife and kids live. The guard starts panicking. Damned if he does and damned if he doesn't; he knows he's screwed. He feels so trapped that he's afraid to talk it out with his friends, the other officers in the cell hall. And he doesn't trust the administration to get him out of the hole he has dug for himself. He assumes they will can him and he has too many bills to pay after his divorce. He hopes and prays that if he plays the mule this one time, the inmate will back off.

Reluctantly the officer hides weed or whatever contraband the inmate is demanding in a VCR tape placed at the bottom of his backpack and approaches the officer at the gate engaging in friendly banter: "How about those Vikings! Did you see the game Monday night?" Here is where most of the officers just "razz" the poor guard whose job it is to go through all his colleagues' lunch boxes, purses and backpacks. He gets through the gate without being caught and one time turns into multiple times. He's been played, he's a fool, and the inmate now has all the power.

Until one day, at the gate during the daily backpack search, he is caught. The officer searching his bag gets lucky and spots something unusual, deeply hidden at the bottom of his backpack. Or the inmate was proactive because he was sick of listening to this guard whine and snitched him out where a "sting" was set up by Internal Affairs. The guard is immediately fired and locked out of the prison.

From that day forward, hanging in the turnkey (the bullet-proof glass booth) is the officer's photo ID and lockout orders, notifying all the officers operating the barred doors not to let him in. And for all of us passing through the turnkey, the officer's nametag is a silent, visual memorial to the guard who was a good guy and a reminder to the rest of us that "these inmates did not get to prison by singing off key in the boys' choir."

Malingering

No inmate shall pretend to be ill or otherwise incapacitated in order to avoid assigned duties or work or shall abuse sick call procedures. Any pretense, false claim, secret action, or intentional act to avoid an assigned task or to conceal a failure to perform a duty also constitutes malingering.

Infraction Penalty

Days (LOP)	Days (RS)	Days (SEG)	Days (PGTL up to)
7-21	3-10	7-30	15

Fakers

In prison, between inmates faking seizures, diabetes or paraplegia, we nurses and guards had seen it all. Seizures were the most common, often so common that when we got the call the officer would just say, "We got a croppie flopper." We knew that was the guard's way of saying the seizure inmate was a fake. Most of the guards were avid fishermen and enjoyed fishing for crappies and invented the saying "croppie flopper," comparing it to the fish "crappie" flopping around the bottom of the boat after being caught. By letting us know it was a "croppie flopper," we knew what kind of emergency it was.

Upon our arrival, sometimes the inmate had already lost his energy from jerking around his bunk or on the floor and was exhausted, already asleep. We knew the inmates who came into the prison on anti-seizure medications and those who did not, but we always checked the medical record before responding to the "code 3 medical" seizure emergency. Other inmates watching from the peanut gallery wanted to make sure that we were taking care of their brother, so many times we gave more attention than needed to make sure the audience viewing us was satisfied with their colleague's care and thus decreased their desire to sue us.

All true seizure inmates were housed on the flag, for safety reasons. One inmate living in the Protective Custody Unit (PCU) had a prosthetic arm; at the end of his so-called hand, there was a hook attached, just like Captain Hook in *Peter Pan*. I had one interaction with him during his legitimate seizure on the floor of PCU. When I arrived, I saw his metal hook-hand flapping every which way, endangering himself and any staff that came near him. Without much thought, a guard came over to the inmate and forcefully but securely placed his boot below the shoulder of the hook-flying-arm and stopped the hook movement. In prison one did not think about medical appropriateness; we were more like a MASH unit in that respect.

For years Johnny was known to seizure about once a month. He was so good at it, he could engage his limbs and torso in a convulsive-spasmodic dance for sometimes and hour. When the medical code was called, I would go to his cell, sit next to him on his bunk and just talk quietly to him, saying, "Come on, Johnny, it's time to relax, let's take a deep breath and slow down," over and over, until he was done. I'd say, "You feel better now, Johnny?" With his eyes closed, he would nod. "Good. Time for you to sleep...'Night, Johnny."

Miller showed up one day admitted to our hospital ward asking for his insulin. He knew his dose and preferred that we give him his shot. Once after I shot him in his upper arm, he smiled at me serenely and said, "Nurse, you give a good shot." This went on for a few days until we got his medical records from another facility where it stated that he was not a diabetic. We were flabbergasted. Who in their right mind would want a needle and medication shot into his arm twice a day? He was discharged and the last time I saw him he was trying to fake lower leg paralysis. He somehow got hold of a pair of crutches and he was slowly dragging his useless legs down the long hallway to the "chow hall" with that same angelic smile on his face.

Ricky, hands down, won the Academy Award for faking. His code 3 medical was out in the industry's carpentry area where we found him about fifteen feet high up on top of a pile of wood, his body in a V shape stuck between layers of large pieces of lumber used in the wood shop. I thought, "Oh, this is bad. How are we going to get him out without using a crane?" An officer and I climbed up onto the woodpile. I got under his arms and the officer got under his legs and we pulled him straight up, hoping we did not paralyze him. A backboard arrived and we placed Ricky very carefully on it. Several officers and I slowly carried him down to the waiting gurney. Our prison doctor was still in Health Services and quickly ordered back X-rays. We again very slowly transferred him onto the X-ray table where the tech scanned his back, chest and pelvis. Ricky was very dramatic and was not cooperative on the table, crying and carrying on about how much pain he was in until we went to the narcotics cabinet and medicated him. First mistake. Our radiologist had not read the X-rays yet, but our doctor read them and stated they were negative. We admitted Ricky to the hospital ward where we would be able to watch him that night to make sure he didn't get any worse. That evening Ricky went into a complete meltdown, complaining of excruciating pain, carrying on and on about how miserable he was with this terrible back pain. The evening nurse decided to rule out a hidden spinal fracture by sending him by ambulance to our security hospital. Second mistake.

For a day or two we were all very nervous that we had moved a spinal fracture patient who would probably be paralyzed from the waist down for life. We figured he would come back in a wheelchair, ready to sue all of us for every penny we had or could possibly make in our lifetime—until the security nurse called from the hospital stating that they had re-X-rayed Ricky and followed up with an MRI, finding there were no fractures or any abnormalities. He was discharged and on his way back to prison.

Ricky arrived cuffed, sitting in the back seat of one of the State cars. The officers were calling for a wheelchair to transport him into the cell hall from the street. I argued with the guard, asking why did he need a wheelchair? The guard stated Ricky couldn't walk. Once I arrived with the wheelchair I was reluctant to let Ricky get into it; with no fractures there wasn't any reason he couldn't walk into the prison. Because Ricky was not cooperating and I wasn't helping, the guard took over and helped Ricky and his lifeless legs from the car to the wheelchair and back into his cell, which had now been moved to the flag. Third mistake.

From that day forward, Ricky decided not to walk again and demanded that his meals be sent to his cell or he needed a wheelchair to get around. He got both. Fourth mistake.

Within a few days, Ricky decided he was a paraplegic and needed daily help with dressing and bathing; therefore, we couldn't accommodate him in our facility and he had to be transferred to the prison hospital at Oak Park. Last I heard, Ricky decided he was so impaired that he couldn't even try to dress himself; therefore, the nurses were on the floor putting his socks on. Fifth and final mistake.

At one point we were housing several wheelchair inmates in our Health Services ward; some were legit and some weren't. Inmate Collins's crime was being on top of a garage and shooting down at some person who was after him. But he supposedly was a paraplegic and wheelchair-bound. How he got on that roof while being in a wheelchair was beyond me.

We had inmate janitors called "swampers" who worked and lived in the hospital. One senior swamper we called The Captain told me that at night there were more guys walking around in that ward than "wheelin." Yet we were assigned to make sure they got bathed!

Besides being inmates, Johnny, Miller, and Ricky had one thing in common: in their daily prison lives, any attention, even if it was negative, was better than no attention at all.

26. Interference with Personnel in the Course of Duties

No inmate shall, in any manner, impede, obstruct, or handicap any correctional personnel in the performance of their duties. Any attempt to impede the free movement of personnel through intimidation, blocking passage; encirclement or physical restraint shall constitute an aggravation of this charge.

Infraction Penalty

Days (LOP)	Days (RS)	Days (SEG)	Days (PGTL up to)
	3-10	30-90	45

Aggravated Penalty

Days (LOP)	Days (RS)	Days (SEG)	Days (PGTL up to)
		90-360	180

Time's Up

If you take away a criminal's freedom, drugs and associates, you are able to catch a glimpse of that person and who he was meant to be before he got into trouble. Nine times out of ten, there's a good guy underneath that sentence. Most were born into situations where they had no control over their environment and thus as little sponges they absorbed all that was surrounding them. Like Ralph Chavous "*Plukey*" Duke, who will never see the light of day.

A diabetic sentenced to life in a federal prison for being the biggest drug lord in Minnesota, Plukey told me that cocaine was so common in his home that it was on his family's breakfast table—where most families had a bowl of sugar on their table, his had a bowl of cocaine. He grew up with it. From his stories it sounded more like he didn't use it as much as he sold it. I didn't follow his trial in the newspapers but saw him every morning in a holding cell as he was waiting to be taken to court. My relationship with him was over his diabetes. He used insulin twice a day and therefore we had frequent interactions and chats while he measured his insulin and gave himself a shot. Because he was a Federal inmate, he was housed on the top tier of the segregation unit reserved for Federal detainees. Once he was sentenced, he would move out of our State prison to a Federal prison. His trial went on for weeks and the last time we spoke he said, "Nurse, I'm going away for a really long time. I am very grateful for the time spent here with you nurses. Thank you."

Another diabetic, Joe, a gay African American man probably in his thirties, doing time for I don't know what reason, happened to be walking with me one morning, up to the Health Services building to get his insulin shot. At the same time, the bell rang for all the workers and students to get to their scheduled buildings for work or class. Therefore hundreds of inmates were outside, all heading to the industry buildings. Now, Mac was a local kid who grew up in the ghetto of St. Paul, Minnesota. Another kid whose ticket was written at birth, in and out of juvenile detention centers until he aged into the prison system for stealing some gold chalices out of a Catholic church. I knew him all too well because he was a frequent flyer in prison and liked to joke around with me and the other nurses.

Walking with Joe, we headed west, up the stairs away from the herd of inmates going north to the industry buildings. We both heard someone yelling below the steps, "Heyyyyyyyy Nurse!" We stopped and turned to see Mac waving to me, his hand holding a banana over his head. I turned and waved and kept on walking. He yelled again and we stopped and turned once more to see him taking the banana and placing it between his thighs. This brought uproarious laughter from his literally captive audience. I stopped and stared at him. Left to right I slowly shook my head, and he knew I wasn't happy. I walked into the Health Services building and immediately wrote him up. After so many years working in prison, this was honestly the first time an inmate who wasn't mentally ill had crossed a line with me.

In writing my report there was an area to write in names of witnesses to the event. So I placed Joe's name there, not giving it a thought. Mac was given a copy of my complaint against him and had enough time to let his fellow cellmates know who the key witness was before he was cuffed and escorted to the Segregation Unit. The protocol was fair and civilized when inmates were written up by staff; they had a chance to tell their side of the story in a kangaroo-type court and they were represented by an ombudsman.

The next morning during the diabetic run, Joe arrived and wanted to speak privately with me. I took him into the exam room and he started to cry and in a panicky voice said that a few of the "brothers" came to his cell the night before and informed him that if he helped me, they would hurt him. Through tears, he was very apologetic that he couldn't be my witness, and I assured him it was in error that I put his name down. I shouldn't have.

We had our day in kangaroo court and I represented myself while the ombudswoman asked me questions about my relationship with Mac. I agreed that "yes, we joked around and until the banana incident, we got along fine." What hurt Mac's case, besides his inappropriate antics, was that he stopped me not once but twice while I was trying to go to work. The ruling was 30 days in "seg" for **Violation #1 Loitering** and **#26 Interference with Personnel in Course of Duties.**

I didn't see Mac until he got out of "seg" but when I did, we were passing each other through the unlocked side door into the main hallway. He was alone and so was I. He immediately started berating me like a jilted boyfriend that I shouldn't have written him up because he was scheduled to be released the very next day, but instead, he spent an extra 30 days in the "hole." I retaliated, got right in his face and strongly stressed to him that it was time for him to grow up!

At that moment it struck me like a "lock in a sock" that I was arguing with a convicted felon. I quickly reached the conclusion that in dealing with difficult patients—aka inmates—I had lost my balanced, nursing perspective and it was time for a change.

I started looking around and without leaving the prison system found that a temporary position was open while a Head Nurse at Lino Lakes Correctional Facility was out on medical leave. I applied and was accepted. This prison was a medium security facility with no armed tower guards, just razor barbed wire and one guard tower. The commute was over forty-five minutes and the only traffic I saw was deer. Lino housed higher-functioning inmates; many of them were working on computers in telemarketing jobs. At the time, the inmates were housed in a dormitory-type setting while getting closer to the end of their sentences.

I was hired as the temporary Head Nurse and in the beginning didn't mind the commute much. I did love the laid-back feel of a medium security facility; it was heaven compared to the ticking time bomb at Stillwater Prison. But all that changed once the Department of Corrections decided to have Lino, not Stillwater, become the new receiving facility for all new inmates. This changed the landscape at Lino. Immediately the warehousing areas where many of the current inmates worked turned into housing units full of bunk beds. Everything at Lino changed, gone were the Monday-Friday day jobs the nurses had held for years. With the increase in population, the nursing services also had to increase, including a nurse to cover the 3-11 p.m. shift and the day and evening shifts over the weekends. This sent the older nurses over the edge and several retired. That left me one part-time local nurse, and a couple of nurses I recruited from Stillwater. Within a few months I made sure that everyone was retrained on the use of oxygen, the crash cart and emergency procedures and I opened a pill window in the cafeteria so the guards didn't have to pass medications anymore.

With the change in Lino's inmate population, so did the type of inmates Lino would now be housing. No longer were the college-bound-type inmates going to be sent to Lino; in fact, those with shorter sentences at Stillwater were on their way to Lino. That and getting beat out of the permanent Head Nurse position by a nurse who only had one month more seniority in the State system than I had, sent me again job searching.

Luckily for me, the doctors from St. Paul Ramsey Medical Center who came to the prison for our secret HIV clinics needed a research nurse and they chose me. Within a month I left the prison system with all its dysfunctions, scarred but ready to tackle a new area of nursing. And from that day forward, the first question out of the interviewer's mouth for every position I applied for over the next twenty years was, "You worked in a prison, wow what was that like?"

Tier 4:

Seg inmate holding a mirror.

Icky Inmates and
One Strange Guard

Micky was a bad apple. He started his criminal career simply enough, stealing fish, until he went to the absolute extreme and murdered an innocent woman. I first met Micky during a lockdown while I was delivering his insulin to the second tier on a very hot and humid Minnesota summer day. I was sweating and not in a good mood. Micky seemed to sense this by saying to me, "You don't know who I am?" *What arrogance*, I thought, and yes, I had read about his grotesque crime in the newspaper. Brutal, savage murder where he dismembered his victim and left her in a garbage bag north of my home. I didn't take his bait and did not reply. My attitude toward him didn't change that day and for the next eight years, I treated him the same as my first encounter. In my eyes he was a sick sociopath using his diabetes to make sure he always had leverage over us because if his health was jeopardized in any way, he had a lawsuit ready to file. I still cringe at this thought but ...not surprisingly, Micky was hired to work in the kitchen as the prison butcher.

I quickly replaced the only 3-11 p.m. nurse who became spooked by an inmate who somehow got her home phone number. She was a new mom and the inmate asked her once, how was "little Bobby" and she immediately quit. Upon meeting this inmate, I could see why she abruptly left Corrections. My first encounter with him:

111

Everyone was locked in their cells and I was alone on a tier (within the guard's view), in front of a very large African American male standing pressed up to his cell bars with his hands dangling outside, ready to grab me if he wished. I wasn't on the tier to see him but he stopped me and started ranting that the only reason I worked in the prison was because "you couldn't get a job anywhere else. All of you nurses are incompetent, and you're all pathetic losers." His looming presence was menacing, his eyes were filled with hate. I could see why he was locked up; this was a guy I'd be watching for. Later on while doing his time, he was sent to segregation for pulling the hair of a female officer as she passed his cell, yanking her hair so hard it whiplashed her neck.

After eight years I transferred to a medium security prison called Lino Lakes where I assumed the position of acting head nurse while that nurse was on a sick leave. I was asked to open a pill window in the cafeteria where the inmates would stop by during their lunch and pick up their medications. This new practice eliminated the officers' duty of passing out prescription medications, which they wanted no part of anyway. The pill window space was taken from part of an existing room where all the office supplies were stored; therefore, a fence was hung to make a clear and secure division of the two spaces, with no crossing over. My space could fit maybe two people and my cart of medications. The inmates built a Dutch door where I could unlock the upper half and have a counter to place medications on. The sergeant in charge of the supplies took his job very seriously and when placing an order with him, he decided how many boxes of, let's say, Kleenex, would be delivered. Thus, if you ordered twelve boxes, you might get four and this was during the flu season. Why he had the last say, I don't know, but he was an intimidating man and no one challenged him for years, until I showed up.

While writing updates from the health services unit and submitting them to the prison newspaper, I became familiar with the inmates who worked as reporters, writers and artists. One Native American named Ben was a very talented artist whose work I admired. I had an idea for a cartoon to be drawn by Ben where he introduced the pill window by placing me inside it, passing a medication envelope to an inmate with my left hand, while my right hand was holding long-handled tongs gripping a box of Kleenex off a shelf, ready to pull it through the fencing behind me. I ran my idea by him and he was a bit hesitant but game, as long as he did not sign his work. A week went by and Ben returned with a perfect illustration of my cartoon idea. He even wrote my name on my lab coat so if there was any trouble, I would clearly be responsible.

Before the prison paper was printed, there was a committee or at least one person on staff who reviewed the content for appropriateness. In my case it was the warden. Unbeknownst to me, the warden had shown the sergeant in charge of supplies the cartoon and wanted his approval to print it in the next issue. The warden didn't get the approval.

I decided to have a face-to-face with this supply sergeant, which was a big mistake. He seethingly, verbally abused me, using multiple expletives while stating that if that cartoon was printed, he would have my job, he would sue me, he would find out where I lived and on and on. At this point I was pretty sure I was speaking to an inmate and an inmate in need of psych medications!

After being berated by the psycho guard, that same day I was called into the office of the warden, a man I hadn't met yet. *Great*, I thought, *let's add more insult to injury*. Fred, the warden, was African American and built like a linebacker. He didn't get up when I entered his office; he just sat there holding my cartoon. Soon he grinned, and then loudly belly laughed while stating, "Finally we have someone up here with a sense of humor."

Too bad his sergeant didn't have one because the cartoon was priceless – and it never ran in the prison newspaper.

Nursing Rules, Circa 1789
Special Services Division
Changes in Health Services
by Ellen Kane

Δ No *dirt, rags or bones shall be thrown from the windows. Nurses are to punctually shift the bed and body linen of the patients, fix their sheets one in a fortnight, their shirts one in four days, their drawers and stockings once a week or oftener if found necessary.*

All nurses who disobey orders, get drunk, neglect their patients, quarrel or fight with other nurses, or quarrel with men, shall be immediately discharged.

February 1995

Δ A triangle, simple enough, but not in medical terminology. A triangle means change. There are many reasons this simple symbol can be found in medical charting. Obviously, from the Nursing Rules of 1789, there have been drastic changes in nursing behavior and nursing care. I no longer throw bones out of the health services windows; the new Osha Standards (Occupational Safety and Health Act) made me stop.

Let's look around and see what has Δ'd.

You may have noticed a short nurse type working the 2-10 p.m. shift Monday through Friday. That would be Kathy M., aka Rudolph during Christmas season. You remember she made us wear antlers. She's the bird woman of Alcatraz. A bit eccentric but her positive outlook is very contagious. We are lucky to be the recipients of her silliness, because sometimes we find medication boxes labeled "leeches" filled with gummy worms. Kathy replaced the phantom 3-11 p.m. nurse. [This was an inside joke, there never was a 3-11 evening nurse, the guards did the nursing work]

Lino [Lakes] finally has a certified X-ray technician. He works three days a week when the doctor is on site. That would be Dennis H. aka the guy known to leave the X-ray door unlocked.

Darin H. is a consulting physical therapist who will spend Tuesday afternoons at Lino. Already he has at least twenty-five clients with chronic lower bunk injuries.

[New inmates were now housed in the old warehouse in bunk beds.]

Lino now has a full-time dental assistant to work with Dr. J. and Dr. W. five days a week. That would be Denise P. from MCF-OPH (Minnesota Correctional Facility Oak Park Heights).

Δ The medication distribution system—the pill window—is in; logging all inmate medication in each cottage is out. Pharmacy is filling medication in bags for seven days; for a more controlled medication, 2-3 days. The inmates are familiar with the pharmacy rules and are responsible for their own medications.

Δ A pill window, and they said it couldn't be done. No longer are the inmate's payroll checks coming through the little window in the cafeteria. The inmate pharmacy window will be open three days a week—Tuesday, Thursday and Saturday—during the noon meal.

And that, my friends, are some of the Δ's in Health Services. Stop by and meet some of these strange but new faces. Oh, and watch out for the bones.

(WRITTEN FOR *GOOD INTENTIONS*, THE MINNESOTA CORRECTIONAL FACILITY—LINO LAKES NEWSLETTER, FEBRUARY 1995)

Life Expectancy

Celebrating my fortieth birthday behind bars was memorable. There was a wheelchair waiting for me upon entering the prison and a black banner hanging overhead, "Nurse Kane is 40." Not very subtle. A graveyard cake complete with headstones was in Health Services for all to enjoy. Staff and some of the inmates were wearing black armbands made of crepe paper.

My Corrections career started while I was in my thirties but many COs (Correctional Officers) started in their twenties, where they were required to retire at age fifty-five.

I didn't know then that I wouldn't make it to retirement like some of the nurses had. There was such a negative air in Corrections, with a contagious attitude that this was normal. Not the inmates per se, it was the line staff who felt vulnerable under an administration that didn't always support them. In fact it wasn't uncommon for a guard to be covertly investigated outside of prison. An internal investigator may suddenly appear at the local watering hole pretending to be part of the group and position himself close to the guard who, for example, is rumored to be smuggling drugs into the prison.

My prison coworkers and I never spoke or even knew about the statistics* attached to being a career correctional officer:

- Correctional Officers (COs) have the second highest mortality rate of any occupation.
- 33.5% of all assaults in prisons and jails are committed by inmates against staff.
- A CO's 58th birthday, on average, is their last.
- A CO will be seriously assaulted at least twice in a 20-year career.
- On average a CO will live only 18 months after retirement.
- COs have a 39% higher suicide rate than any other occupation,
- And have higher divorce and substance abuse rates than the general population.

In fact, if we had known these facts, we probably would have scoffed at them. After I left Corrections in the mid '90s, I started hearing about early and tragic deaths of guards I had worked with and I became suspicious of a shorter life expectancy for COs. Young guys committing suicide, death by excessive drinking, or heart attacks in their fifties. Later, in 2018 while writing this piece, I contacted a good friend, a retired lieutenant, who sent me a list he had compiled of suicides from 1982-2004, many by gun. One officer came to work, checked out a gun in the secured area that housed all the firearms, went behind a locker and shot himself right there. Others, who made it to retirement yet were still under sixty years old, died of heart disease, illicit drug use, i.e. cocaine, or just drank themselves to death. In my mind this phenomenon was more than just not taking care of themselves; psychologically, these men and women had been severely traumatized.

While working an evening shift one Thursday night, a Minneapolis police officer dropped off half a dozen newly sentenced inmates. I was paged to come to the front of the prison for the required medical interviews. The police officer, while removing the chains and handcuffs from these guys, asked me how many nurses were working the shift. When I said it was just me, he said, "Man, you're the only nurse on duty? Wow, your job is tough. You guys' jobs working in prison are so much harder than ours on the streets." At the time I thought he was crazy—our inmates weren't usually drunk or stoned with guns and knives readily available like criminals on the streets. But in the long run I now understand what he meant. Seeing the same faces day in and day out in the cell block, with the never-ending mind games being played over and over, had a greater impact than the short-term interactions these cops had with these same inmates on the street. Add the incessant psych games from the inmates with an administration that may not always support its own and it's no wonder the prison guards were left feeling angry, isolated and desperate.

Looking for a first-hand validation on these stressors, I contacted another past coworker and friend, a sergeant now retired after twenty-five years of service. I asked him to reflect on his years in Corrections. Here's what he said:

"Prison life is a violent life. It is a collection of predators from the street all placed in a confined space, preying on each other and staff if they can. It is a very negative environment where you are bombarded by negativity on a constant basis. This environment places an edge on staff, or it did me. You always have your guard up, and chaos can happen at a moment's notice. Over time this edge leans toward aggression and you are 'on deck' for a fight, a confrontation or an argument. This is at work and spills over when not at work. I found that it was impossible to turn off until you are out of the prison system for at least a year.

You work closely with a cell hall full of inmates. You are out-numbered by possibly 200 to 1 at any point. Working out in the yard (recreation) and now it's 500 to 1. You must be able to communicate with them on their level and think like they do to some extent to protect yourself from being set up or just from physical harm. Because inmates are constantly trying to 'get over' on staff, your level of trust is diminished. You trust other staff but not the administration, which has no empathy for your efforts, and no trust for civilians, since they may in fact be trying to set you up on behalf of an inmate. We never trusted an inmate; they were lying because their lips were moving.

As new officers you become isolated from your friends outside of prison because you are assigned a shift that gives you days off in the middle of the week and your old friends don't go out in the middle of the week. Then you realize that people from the street (family and friends) have nothing in common with you and vice versa. You try to talk about 'boarding' inmates or 'hooch,' 'shanks,' 'kites,' or the 'flag' or any other prison-related action or terms, and they look at you confused. What civilian can understand what it means when an inmate 'goes off' or how inmates can enrage you within minutes of contact with them? Correctional Officers understand that.

The process of going from a civilian to becoming like an inmate takes approximately a year. It will be refined over the years but the big chunks have been integrated by then. By the end of your first year, you still may have a wife but you certainly have very few of your old friends. Everything you now do is prison-related. You have a clique that you work, drink, trust and commiserate with about prison life. No one outside the clique would understand what is important to you anymore. The more you work closely with the inmates, and the longer you work with them, you create a rapport. They understand you and you them. Now you too are thinking like an inmate. Not agreeing with them, not giving in to their demands, but acting and thinking more like them than before when you were a civilian. You now know their value system, their pecking order, and their problem-resolution styles. You have become like them more than they will ever become like you. And it works in your favor, especially when in a situation like where you have to shut off the inmate's phones and they have surrounded you, at least thirty of them, yelling about how you're fucking with them. Normal reasoning might not work at this point but presenting it from an inmate's perspective may save your ass. You do have the power and the authority to penalize the inmates, but be very careful how you wield that power; the inmates never forget."

KEVIN E. BEDORE, CANADIAN FEDERAL CORRECTIONAL OFFICER STATES IN HIS ARTICLE, PUBLISHED 8/27/2012. **

Beating The Odds

"I have also talked with far too many younger officers who have just begun their careers. They hate their lives so much they are almost guaranteeing the bad outcomes presented at the beginning of the article. Some commit suicide on a weekly plan by the amount of alcohol and tobacco they consume. Many don't exercise, get enough sleep or watch what they eat and wonder why they feel so poorly. The worst thing I see far too often is officers who are so fixated on getting out of the system and retiring (usually early but not always) that they wish their lives away. This in law enforcement circles is called 'ROD' or 'retired on duty.' This person is a burnout who wears a uniform and doesn't do the work expected of him or her. He or she is held captive to this dysfunctional state by one or more of the factors mentioned. Not surprisingly, the ugly stats at the beginning are all about those types. To top matters off, working with RODs makes everybody else's job harder and more dangerous because you must take up their slack, oftentimes at the expense of having nobody watching your own back."

** REPRINTED WITH THE AUTHOR'S PERMISSION AS NOTED IN CORRECTIONS.COM.

As statistics predicted, another past coworker, Lieutenant Howard McClish died a few years after his retirement, but it wasn't from his career in Corrections, it was from diabetes. As the Recreational Lieutenant, he was constantly filling the inmates' days with activities he programmed. He would organize teams for basketball and softball, and bring in outside teams to play against the inmates. His assistant, the rec officer, always made sure all the bats, weights and other equipment were accounted for before letting the inmates go back to their cells. One Saturday, he organized a full marathon of 26.2 miles, yet the track was only a quarter mile long. Several inmates ran the full marathon, along with one of our nurses and some staff members. One Native American inmate ran the whole marathon barefoot.

For several years I worked the evening shift during Lt. McClish's tenure in recreation and I can't recall once being called out to the rec yard, the weight room or the gym for any assaults or fights. Usually these prison areas were notorious for assaults. Sports, Lt. McClish knew, would keep the inmates active and thus tired and less aggressive. But state funding was cut and administration converted the gym area into a receiving area where bunk beds were placed. One inmate upon returning to prison told me he woke up where he believed the boxing ring used to be. Recreation came to a halt, basically eliminated, and warehousing inmates became the new norm in the 1990s, as it still is today.

Sadly, the first documented murder of a Minnesota Correctional Officer happened recently at Stillwater Prison on Wednesday July 18, 2018. The inmate, in for murder, attacked the CO in the prison industry area with a hammer. This officer was well liked and had sixteen years of service. This extreme act of violence was always the worst fear for all correctional staff, one that would daily erode their mental health and ultimately, unknowingly, shorten their lives.

*STATISTIC SOURCES: *STRESS MANAGEMENT FOR THE PROFESSIONAL CORRECTIONAL OFFICER*, DONALD STEELE, PH.D., STEELE PUBLISHING 2001.*CORRECTIONS YEARBOOK 2000, 2002*, CRIMINAL JUSTICE INSTITUTE, MIDDLETOWN, CT. *SOURCEBOOK OF CRIMINAL JUSTICE STATISTICS 2003.* BUREAU OF JUSTICE STATISTICS, 31ST EDITION, NCJ 208756. *SUICIDE RISK AMONG CORRECTIONAL OFFICERS*, ARCHIVES OF SUICIDE RESEARCH, STACK, S.J. & TSOUDIS, O. 1997. *METROPOLITAN LIFE ACTUARIAL STATISTICS*, 1998 SOCIETY OF ACTUARIES, 1994

POST-PRISON

Y es, they do get out and sometimes they move into your neighborhood. My first encounter with an inmate outside of prison was in a parking lot in downtown St. Paul, Minnesota. I was headed to the St. Paul Hotel to celebrate my parents' fortieth wedding anniversary with my family. I noticed when I pulled into the lot that the parking attendant in the booth looked familiar. *Oh lord*, I thought, *I know him from prison*, thinking the inmate may not recognize me—after all, I was out of the white lab coat and in a dress, heels and panty hose! During my whole career, my daily uniform was jeans and a lab coat; my legs were never shown. I quickly exited my car and bee-lined away from his booth as he was making eye contact with me.

My parents' anniversary dinner was fantastic—lots of laughs, good food, and many of my brothers and sisters in attendance. However, all through dinner I couldn't shake this ominous feeling about walking alone, in the dark, to the parking lot. I didn't want to put a damper on the mood so I quietly mentioned to my brother Kevin my concern about the ex-inmate, now parking attendant. He said, "No problem, I will give you a ride to your car."

The dinner ended, we said our goodbyes, and my brother and I walked to his car parked a few blocks from the hotel. Pulling up to the parking lot, my brother could only drop me off outside the entrance so I said goodbye to him and he had to drive away because of the cars behind him moving him along. I was hoping as I headed to my car that the ex-inmate had punched out and had left the area. I was pretty close to my car when a male voice started yelling, "Nurse, Nurse, hey Nurse!" Just my luck, there he was, sprinting between cars, dying to get my attention.

He caught up to me as I was opening my door, so I stood between the open door and the driver's seat. He was pleasant and happy to see me. He just wanted me to know that he was doing really well and the Atlantis program (chemical dependency unit in prison) had really worked for him. Now I remembered him as a nice kid who was sick a few times while doing his time with us. I wished him well and told him I didn't want to see him again. He laughed and went back to parking cars. I called my brother to yell at him for driving away but he said he didn't leave me; he had pulled over and was watching until I drove away.

I often saw familiar faces on the street while running clinical trials for HIV/AIDS drugs from Hennepin County Medical Center in downtown Minneapolis. One ex-inmate saw my nameplate outside my office door in the hospital and stopped by my office every time he had a doctor's appointment. He happened to be one of my brother Dennis's juvenile offenders and was a hell of a basketball player in prison. This inmate never knew that his probation officer and I were brother and sister, and it was my brother who taught him how to play basketball. When he stopped by, our conversation was always focused on him and what progress he was making while staying out of prison. I encouraged him to keep playing basketball and to get involved in the local public gyms with the coaches, to help mentor kids on the game and also how to stay away from crime.

Several HIV/AIDS ex-inmates followed their prison doctors to the county hospital once they were released and I would see them in the clinic during their appointments. Some would sign up for a research study their doctor was conducting because they could get their HIV medications, blood work, and follow-up appointments all covered under the study protocol. Plus, an added bonus, they got to see me and if they didn't show up, they knew I would be looking for them.

One memorable HIV inmate housed in our Health Services ward was a carnival worker. He had the personality of a circus barker with a Texas twang and many times had all of us staff and inmates laughing during his carnival stories. He was released and showed up in the county hospital while I was recruiting patients for a study. I was not sure he would be a good study patient but I took him into a private office anyway and went over with him all the details of the study and his requirements. After a lengthy discussion, we went over the patient's consent and I asked him if he had any questions. He said, "Yes, I do." He said, "Will you marry me?" Needless to say, he turned out to not be a good study patient; I found out at the end of the two-year trial that while his blood work always remained stable, he never took any of the study medication. This led us to believe that because his labs never changed, he was being maintained on the HIV drug and not the placebo. His explanation was that now he had two years of very expensive medications for when he does get sick and can't afford the drugs.

Last time I saw the carnival worker, he caught up to me leaving the hospital in the parking lot while walking to my car. He was wondering if there were any more studies he could enroll in like the last one. "Nothing on the horizon," I said. I told him I would keep him in mind and we said goodbye. As I was pulling forward to the exit, he flew out of nowhere and landed on my car hood. Laughing, he rolled off the hood to the pavement, hoping to gather attention from others so they'd think I just hit him and they were his witnesses. But instead of checking for injuries, I backed up, rolled down the window and yelled at him to keep moving or this time I was really going to run him over!

Yes, they do get out of prison and many stay out for good but there are others who reoffend or violate their parole just to get inside, away from the bitter Minnesota winters.

Dressing up for an employee's going away party
with a couple of the hospital's swampers.

The Prison Mirror:
"It's Never Too Late To Mend"

"**H**ello, I would like to order a subscription to the *Prison Mirror*. Can you help me with that?"

"Yes, of course," answered a deep male voice. "That would be $2.00 an issue or $24.00 for a year."

"Ok, I would like to order a year's subscription, please."

"Great. You need to make a check or money order out to the finance department. Here is the address… We are currently working on the September issue."

"Oh, wow, it's December. How come the paper is coming out so late?"

"Well, we have one cell hall in lockdown, and we had *dat* murder, you know."

"Yes, I heard about that. So tragic. Such a horrible, senseless crime."

"Yes."

"Well, thank you for your time and I look forward to my first issue." (December 6, 2018).

The *Prison Mirror* is the oldest continuously published prison newspaper in the United States. On the front cover of each issue is the motto, *It's Never Too Late To Mend.*

The story is that in 1887 fifteen inmates raised, then loaned, $200 to get the newspaper underway. Three of the inmates were thought to be the Younger brothers, Cole, Bob, and Jim, who were doing their time for robbing the bank in Northfield, Minnesota, on September 7,1876. All three brothers were part of the Jesse James gang, serving life sentences for the robbery and death of two Northfield residents during the robbery.

At first, the newspaper published weekly ads from the merchants of the town of Stillwater, Minnesota. The price per year for an outside subscription was $1.00. Eventually, as years went by, the editors realized that the inmates were not prospective customers and dropped the ads.

During the years I worked at Stillwater Prison, I looked forward to the biweekly publication of the *Prison Mirror*. It became an award-winning newspaper and was judged first place in the printed prison newspaper competition that was entered by 22 other prison publications. The judges were faculty members of the Department of Journalism at Western Kentucky University in Bowling Green, Kentucky. The yearly American Penal Press Awards was sponsored by the School of Journalism at Southern Illinois University in Carbondale, Illinois.

In 1986 *The Prison Mirror* had a circulation of 2,800; inmates and staff received free copies. Subscribers outside the prison paid $5.00 a year for 26 issues. Among them were judges, attorneys, families of inmates, and ex-inmates. Subscribers lived in all 50 states and three foreign countries: Canada, South Africa, and Sweden.

During the eighties and early nineties, sports inside the prison usually dominated three to six pages of the newspaper. Featured were action photos, team analyses, plus anecdotes reported by the current sports editor. In the February 26, 1988, issue, Jahi Sadiki thoughtfully dissected the Varsity basketball team in his sports column, writing: "There are too many individuals on the Varsity now that prescribe [sic] to the *I am the greatest, back alley, Michael Jordan clone type basketball*, they find excuses to blame everyone but themselves ...The Varsity basketball team hasn't played a game this season that they didn't criticize one of their teammates, referee's, coaches, or somebody in the stands watching...they blame everyone but themselves. On the other foot, is the Varsity player who comes to play by the rules of the game, to compete as an athlete while giving his best, and above all, has fun while playing the game. He is the team player, the real winner ... If winning at any cost without sacrifice or discipline is the name of the game, you can have it, and you can put it where the sun don't shine."

Besides basketball, weather permitting, softball, handball, boxing, weightlifting and 5K races with an annual 26-mile marathon kept the inmates active. The 1986 event was called Marathon-in-the-Round; the course consisted of running 112 times around a designated quarter-mile track. One of the fastest runners, a Native American named Fred, always ran these marathons barefoot.

In 1985, Robert E. Taliaferro, a temporary inmate from Wisconsin, was named Editor of the *Prison Mirror* where, for the next four years, he took pride in "his" publication. He wanted to be competitive so his first order of business was to request computers. Computers in a prison in 1985 were rare. There was one computer in our medical records room that only the medical records staff could use. It wasn't until I left Corrections in 1995 that I was allowed to have a computer all to myself as a research nurse. But the staff writers of the *Prison Mirror* each had a computer and were able to publish award-winning newspapers that won first place for Best Printed Prison Newspaper for the years 1985, 1986 and 1988.

Taliaferro wrote a column he called "Peekin'," where he reported, mostly tongue-in-cheek, about the news inside the walls. Many of his columns were Peekin' into cell halls, the mess hall, the yard, the warden's office, and so on. Never using employees' names, he got away with poking fun at the warden, officers, inmates, and always the employee responsible for the food.

In the June 16, 1989, issue of the *Prison Mirror*, Taliaferro wrote his last "Peekin'" column prior to his transfer back to a Wisconsin prison. His most notable quotes from that column are as follows—and please note he is calling himself a "sage."

> *"Peekin' around the publication's office, the peekin' sage is experiencing a little remorse ... or is it gas?*
>
> *"For those that have been supportive of the column, the sage sends out his sincere words of appreciation, and for those that did not like the column ... what the hell, 'it be like that sometimes.'*
>
> *"If the sage hurt anyone's feelings over the four years of the column's life, sorry about that ... I would have the violins play a concerto but the damn things are all packed up."*
>
> *"'Peekin'' was designed to give some insight into the mundane things which go on in the prison which were comical or simply just plain stupid."*
>
> *"If the sage were to list his favorites (columns), they would be the guy who mooned the population in the big yard; the mad rush from the men during the health fair a few year ago; and the attack of the killer bats."*

"So for the final little barb ... I mean, what are you going to do, send me to Wisconsin? Peekin' around the hall-ways over the last few years, the sage has always wondered, Why does everyone call the warden 'Uncle Bob'? *The sage looked at his photo the other day and thought,* Funny, he doesn't look like anyone's uncle in here. *The sage always thought that was interesting, but then he has heard wardens called worse ... so I guess it's not all that bad."*

By 1993, the recreation program dwindled, due to a drastic increase in population. Where there was once a gym, new arrivals were now sleeping in bunks on the basketball floor. This change affected the newspaper's sports coverage, limiting it to one or two pages. Now, twenty-five years later, in 2018, the *Prison Mirror* still only dedicates a couple of pages to sports events; one page usually is a crossword puzzle, Sudoku, and various word games. Softball season still has many teams playing against each other, but with less commentary on the actual game. In the August 2018 issue, sports reporter Ronald Greer reported scores and stats with a few notable lines from one game: "An inmate in A-West went on the disabled list after breaking his wrist diving for a short pop fly in the outfield. When asked what happened, he said, "I broke it. But guess what? I caught that [expletive]."

Notably, I've found that in 25 years the overall theme of the newspaper hasn't changed. Yes, the size of the actual paper is smaller, the "Peekin'" column is gone, and there is less sports reporting, but the inmates' art and poems are still published, with space given to articles reprinted from news outlets, promoting rehabilitation and education for inmates who will one day leave prison.

Today's *Prison Mirror* seems more relevant to the times, where people are listening to efforts dealing with prison reform, rehabilitation, and restorative justice, instead of just building more prisons. Yes, some will never leave prison and shouldn't, but for the ones who will, *It's Never Too Late To Mend* still holds true, 130 years later.

HTTPS://WWW.NYTIMES.COM/1987/08/11/US/THE-PRISON-MIRROR-A-NEWSPAPER-MARKS-ITS-100TH-YEAR.HTML

Poem:
Morning Men
by
Ellen Kane

Beware the morning men approaching your parking lot.

"Ma'am, don't mean you no harm, ma'am" plead the morning men.

You keep walking swiftly, hoping to pass
the danger, north of the lot.

Its 6:30 a.m. You walk with strength and
power, your purse close to your body.

Your backpack, holding no valuables, intrigues the morning men.

Not that you would, but you have nothing
to neither barter nor lobby.

You are a single mom walking alone on your way to work.

Always on alert, for you worked in a prison
and know the morning men.

Familiar faces you pass on the streets,
released but now they seem to lurk.

Last month a nurse entering the front door
had her bag snatched from her.

And she struggled for her packed lunch away
from one of the morning men.

He was young and anxious with no
weapon, yet he was not deterred.

With your three boys in college, there are no hopes of retiring soon.

Happy in your work and relieved your boys
won't become morning men.

But you are saddened by these boys wandering
homeless under this pale moon.

So you keep walking, faster now, as you are only a half block away.

Approaching the bus stop where usually
there are several morning men.

Today there is only one, an older man, poor in
appearance but clean for the workday.

He has a kindness and concern in his eyes so you don't look away.

He speaks as you pass. "Beware the morning
men, for they are out today."

Nurse Kane with inmate runners at a prison
muscular dystrophy fundraiser, in 1987.

Epilogue

When I started writing my prison stories, I had no idea what would happen to them, or who would be interested in them. What was I trying to say about these inmates and my decade spent in their midst?

But as I kept writing, I realized that I was in fact telling my readers about a period of history whose importance I wasn't even aware of at the time. Those years from 1985-1995 were the height of mass drug incarcerations in the U.S, whose goal was to imprison all people having anything to do with selling, manufacturing, or using drugs, no matter how minor the offense.

"Get tough on crime." "Just say no." "This is your brain on drugs." Numerous anti-drug campaigns resulted in so many arrests that maximum-security prisons started double bunking, even though keeping inmates separated in cells was a much safer way to run a prison. But there was no room, so bunk beds went up in areas that were once used for industry work programs. Cots went into recreation areas so there was less room for inmates to work off steam. All across the U. S., it was men who were most often incarcerated for drug crimes, but women too were caught up in this sweep. Women who loved their men enough to smuggle drugs into prison visiting rooms, risked their children's livelihoods as well as their own. Little did they know how the repercussions of their actions would haunt them and their families for the rest of their lives.

Today, in 2019 we are seeing much needed changes in drug laws and how we treat the mentally ill. Most mentally ill people on prescribed treatment, do not commit crimes. To date, the mentally ill inmate is not being locked up for acting crazy. The practice is just starting but we now have systems in place for treatment not punishment.

Cannabis, aka marijuana, is no longer a bad word. Legalization in many states stops the underworld's control. But the damage is done for those who are still doing time for drug convictions twenty years ago. While researching the history of mass incarceration I read an editorial in the L.A. Times from Chesa Boudin, public defender in San Francisco. Knowing first hand, as his parents were both inmates, Chesa is currently running for District Attorney in San Francisco; he is a passionate leader in criminal justice reform. He is one of many that want to fix our broken system of racial disparities and mass incarceration and change society by creating a national model for a more sensible effective response to crime.

In closing, ask yourself... in your younger days have you ever driven drunk, stole something, bought a bag of weed, dropped acid, or snorted cocaine, but were never caught? Appreciate the fact that you could be living a life entirely different from the one you are living today. As Emily Baxter states in her book... _We Are All Criminals_.

Acknowledgements:

Stillwater State Prison employees: Drs. Ramos, Eyunni, Sullivan, Thurn, Schwebke, Lamey and Eoyang. Dentists: Chuck, Wayne and Mark. **Special departments**: Linda, Joyce, Brian F., Maurine, Sherry and S.Huot **Nurses:** Jean B., Della, Jeannie S., Bette, Evern, Winnie, Evelyn, John, Kathy D., Diane, Kathy M. Suzanne, Hank, Scott, Mary C. **Officers:** Vito, Howard, Gary F., Lou C., Frankie P., Pat R., Mike S., Harmon, Paul N., Gary P., G. Stahley, T. Murphy, J. Donald. **Stillwater Wardens:** Robert Erickson and Dennis Benson

Lino Lakes Prison employees: Warden: G.Fred Lefeur and Special Services Director, Jo Earhart, and Nurse Janis

Commissioners of Corrections: Orville Pung, and Sheryl Ramstad Vass

Thank you to Gary Senser: C/o Botello & Senser ReMax, Real Estate, Manhattan Beach, CA for his daily ear and technical support.

Thank you to Lori LoCicero: Cofounder of DEATH DECK for her author expertise and advice.

IN MEMORY OF LT. HOWARD MCCLISH
1947-2005